31,18

WINDOWS ON HENRY STREET

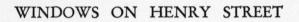

THE SKY LINE OF HENRY STREET

WINDOWS ON HENRY STREET

By

LILLIAN D. WALD

With Drawings from Life by
JAMES DAUGHERTY

BOSTON
LITTLE, BROWN, AND COMPANY
1939

THE ATLANTIC MONTHLY PRESS BOOKS
ARE PUBLISHED BY
LITTLE, BROWN, AND COMPANY
IN ASSOCIATION WITH
THE ATLANTIC MONTHLY COMPANY

PRINTED IN THE UNITED STATES OF AMERICA

To

ALICE – IRENE – RITA

Comrades who forged out of their interests and their talents many of the programmes for art and education described in this book

FOREWORD TO FOURTH EDITION

THE CAMPUS STIRS TO ACTION

AT the time this book was being written there seemed little evidence of independent thought, of concern with vital social and economic issues of the day, among the college generation. More recently we have begun to note evidence of wholesome disaffection, fearlessly expressed, on the campus and where groups of young people congregate. It therefore seems fitting to add a few lines to what was said in the chapter on "Education and the Arts" regarding the indifference of young people to the real world about them.

Students to-day throughout the land seem to be animated by the consciousness of a need for change, by the vision of a secure, warless world in place of the prevailing chaos which they see around them. The old complacence, inertia, and apparent content with conditions that exist are vanishing. In their place is a developing awareness that all is not right with the world; and this awareness has come to be a determined and articulate effort to do something about it, a responsibility which, as young people see it, is theirs as much as their elders'. Tangible proof of this campus awakening is seen in the organized, aggressive anti-war protest; in collective agitation against militarism and against teachers' loyalty oaths, lynching, and other subversive trends in politics, education, and public affairs. On its positive side this new ferment among youth is finding expression in efforts toward securing social insurance, slum clearance, the abolition of child labor, freedom of economic and political discussion, and the development of a dynamic internationalism.

One illustration occurred on April 12, 1935, when 175,000 students gave realistic evidence of their anti-war sentiments by leaving classrooms and laboratories in order to participate in a nation-wide strike against war, one of the most dramatic and publicized peace demonstrations of our time. Among the groups largely responsible for this demonstration were the Student League for Industrial Democracy and the National Student League. These two lively organizations recently united to form the American Student Union, which bids fair to become a potent force not only for the study of such burning problems as war, poverty, and unemployment, but for organized action in behalf of the solution of these problems. It is gratifying to witness this honest, courageous effort on the part of young people in our colleges and universities to come to grips with reality.

LILLIAN D. WALD

HOUSE-ON-THE-POND
SAUGATUCK, CONNECTICUT

ACKNOWLEDGMENTS

A PROTRACTED illness and slow convalescence have given me unusual detachment from administrative duties, affording opportunity to relate my experiences and observations over an eventful period. As far as possible, every reference, incident, and quotation has been verified, and, where memory was not clear cut, contemporaries have been consulted.

This book could not have been written without the help of Beulah Amidon, whose service was invaluable. Her sympathy, her training, and the years she has spent in research and as editor furnished a background that made it possible for her to recognize immediately what I was trying to express. Her familiarity with the whole field of social endeavor aided the verification of statement. Moreover, the telling of stories was often occasion for great fun, and a joy to the story-teller; the "More, more!" from her explains and perhaps defends the multiple anecdotes, sad and gay, throughout the pages.

Van Wyck Brooks, Connecticut neighbor and helpful friend, months before the book was begun, as we gathered about the open fire, pressed the opinion that another volume should follow *The House on Henry Street.* In this he was abetted by Lee Simonson. Mr.

Brooks often gave his critical appraisal of plans and materials.

Paul U. Kellogg, old friend and comrade in numerous adventures, relived with me the interlude of the Mexican anxiety and the effort of the American Union Against Militarism to adhere as long as possible to the policy of presenting the principles of peace and the practical arguments against war.

I know that the list is not complete, and my indebtedness cannot be fully acknowledged; but appreciation of none is lacking.

Ernest Poole suggested the title. Fannie Hurst and other friends gave thought and final approval to that important clue to a tale.

Florence Clarke refreshed my memory with data on Elizabeth Farrell's work. Harold Kellock, Katharine Amend, Captain Yarrow, read part or all of the Russian chapter. Katharine Lenroot placed at my disposal sacred file reports and correspondence of the U. S. Children's Bureau. Pauline Goldmark, George W. Alger, Dr. Mary H. S. Hayes, Judge Jonah Goldstein, assured me of the accuracy of references to various protective measures for women and children.

Felix Warburg's interest and suggestions never failed in value, and I turned to him for interpretation of some of the ancient ceremonies and superstitions. Bruno Lasker gave me his understanding of settlement development, and Nina Warburg's comments on the written word afforded the helpful judgment of one on the observer's lines.

But, beyond all, the interest and help of the nurses

and the Settlement associates rank high. Marguerite Wales, Elizabeth Mackenzie, Mabel De Bonneval, Jeanne Foster, never lost their patience, and Isabel Stewart, Katharine Tucker, and Dr. Louis I. Dublin generously shared the burden of placing data before me and reading critically the chapters on Nursing and Health.

That so many people took occasion to express their interest in the writing of the book indicated to me, beyond their personal solicitude, the eagerness with which, in this period of change, men and women wish to look through windows that have been opened upon a moving world.

THE AUTHOR

CONTENTS

ILLUSTRATIONS

WINDOWS ON HENRY STREET

I

WHY THIS BOOK IS WRITTEN

THIS is not an autobiography, and it is my belief that no autobiography is wholly true. The autobiographies of people I have known, and with whom I have worked, have often shown a surprising innocence of parallel movements and influences that have greatly affected the things in which the writers were interested — nor is this failing limited to stories of self.

As an example of how unsuspected such influences may be, I recall the effort of our group to keep the "L" loop off Delancey Street. The protest had its beginning in a meeting called at the House on Henry Street, to see what could be done to prevent the extension of the detested encumbrance into our crowded streets — an encroachment that meant not only more noise and dirt and congestion, but also death to our hopes for a broad highway through our part of the city. Charles B. Stover, of unique personality, because of his knowledge and unquestioned sincerity was appointed the chairman. We fought hard: a little group of social workers against powerful business, financial, and political strongholds. We carried our case to the press, and editorials presented our point of view. We held huge meetings. We circulated petitions, and appointed committees. I never left New York City that summer. I attended the "Rapid Transit" meetings. I was afraid something would be put over if I did not sit close. The "L" came as far as the Williamsburg Bridge terminus, and stopped. Then, when Paul Warburg came to this country and was appointed on a committee by the Chamber of Commerce, the question of erecting that loop came up again. He was told it was useless to consider it as a transportation relief, because of "these infuriated social workers." And yet, when publicity was given — through the Ivins Committee — to the financing of certain utilities, it was disclosed that a fee of $50,000 had been paid to one Lemuel Quigg for "accelerating" public opinion *against* this "L" construction, and the word "accelerator" came into vogue. *We* had never heard of Lemuel Quigg. We had not even been aware of his influence, working either for or against us. But in that experience I learned unforgettably that one may struggle on and on, never knowing what other interests may be playing their part in the same effort.

No, this book is not an autobiography. Rather, it is the story of the House on Henry Street since 1915 —

the years that saw war, peace, boom and depression, Russian Revolution, prohibition; it is an attempt to show the place of a settlement in the movements of the day.

Settlements appear frequently in current fiction and in serious publications, but there seems to be limited comprehension of their real significance. One sound appraisal is that of Charles and Mary Beard in *The Rise of American Civilization;* and the New Oxford Dictionary has perhaps most simply and clearly defined the settlement as "an establishment in the poorer quarter of a large city, where educated men and women live in daily contact with the working class for coöperation in social reform." But "settlement" in this sense is a comparatively new word; it is probably unavoidable that sentimentalists and romanticists should see only the outer expression and never realize how simple and logical and yet how significant is the impulse of live-minded people to come together for spiritual adventure.

This book attempts to show the harmonies built up in the community by the many little groups, through their sympathetic relations with other groups; and also to show how effective these group relations often are in dealing with social problems, which may vary in their importance at times, but not in their urgency, from generation to generation. Perhaps some of the complacency with which people are prone to view these problems grows out of the construction put upon the Biblical words, "The poor ye have always with you. . . ." An intrepid leader of my acquaintance insisted that the injunction has not been read with understanding. What was really meant, he said, was this: "Keep the poor always with you; never let them get far from you; hold them in your consciousness, for poverty is a disease in the body politic."

Much that is valuable in settlement life defies wordy description. The best is often the imponderable; also, one experience follows another until one must see the whole chain, not its separate links, to realize its strength and usefulness. Often the best develops from the fact that there is always plan — but not always programme.

Measures for social betterment initiated by the settlements have almost sprung from actual need. Nothing illustrates this better than the acceptance throughout the world of public health nursing. In trying to establish a technique for the care of sick children and the education of mothers, I was moved to say that I should know that our approach and direction were right if what was found to be successful on Henry Street would help the remote mothers in China. And it was not many years before Chinese young women came to us to acquire experience in public health nursing — to get the spirit of Henry Street, as they said, to carry back with them to China. Dr. Yamei Kin, the distinguished physician and social reformer, wrote me: "I wish you could see Hsui Lan at work in Peking. You would think that Henry Street was here."

Perhaps the reason why these neighborhood households have been more effective than their numbers, their resources, or the talents of their members would seem to warrant is the fact that the settlement is the most pliable tool for social service that has been developed. There is nothing in its construction that forbids coöperation and action on whatever may arise from day to day. (The picture of her life in a settlement by Sinclair Lewis's heroine, Ann Vickers, must record a unique experience, for I have been unable to find any who recognize the description as within their knowledge.)

Newcomers to a settlement are often surprised by the natural simplicity of the household, the happy relations that grow out of this kind of living together. At Henry Street, our experience has been rich in the fellowship that is inevitable in a united company. The recognition and the beauty and pleasures of friendship thrive well when the tie that binds is colored with the deeper and more significant purposes of life. Men and women differing widely in their philosophy live together harmoniously, respecting the convictions of all who gather around. Part of the week's usual routine is a "Residents' Meeting," at which some question of current importance is frankly presented and discussed. A vote on the majority opinion is never taken.

Though my pacifism during the War was well known, there were many residents who thought differently; the House was offered and accepted as headquarters for the local Draft Board. We released on full salary one of the most able members of our staff, to serve as chairman of the Draft Board, that the regulations might be so administered as to minimize the anxiety and fear of the men and their families. Many of our boys became officers, and were reported to have done good work. Despite the known personal conviction of the Head Worker, there was scarcely one boy who left without coming for her blessing and good wishes, and the correspondence from camp and overseas was faithfully sustained.

The House buzzed with war activities. Never did the call from Washington or elsewhere for help on protective nursing measures fail to secure immediate response. And when the War ended I was sent on a diplomatic passport to the International Conference at Cannes, where health and child welfare for almost the entire world were discussed. This pleasing understanding prevailed throughout the neighborhood, and people of all the nations under arms met at clubs, at parties, and at picnics. Visitors came in uniform and in mufti, accepting us for what we were.

A stranger once fell into chat with a policeman on Henry Street and their talk turned to the landmarks of the neighborhood. The Settlement he identified for the visitor as "the house where, if the King of England came to America, he'd be sure to be taking lunch with the ladies there." Evidently the cop had his own measure of us. And, while reigning royalty has not honored us, we have found that a neutral place with no frontiers does attract interesting people. I like to think of those who have crossed our threshold, the distinguished and the great unknown. They have brought much to Henry Street!

The goal of a social programme based on personal interests is to help individuals to the highest level of which each is capable, not forgetting that wrong may be done by overreaching as much as by underprivilege. But as windows open we often see that what is good

THE HOUSE ITSELF

for the individual is also good for the many. No organization proceeds far with a fixed idea. Intelligence, disinterestedness, and respect for people will show how best they can be served. Stagnation is sure to follow an inelastic programme or a belief in a single road which all of us must follow.

I hold to my faith that the first essential to sound human relations is respect. No one who has that sense of respect will patronize, or insult, or feel alien to, human beings. It is not only good common sense, but the basis for friendship and understanding that endure.

Emphasis is repeatedly laid on the interrelationships of individuals and of groups, even the large and sometimes unwieldy groups we call nations. We are now accustomed to seeing governments, through their representatives, come together to get acquainted before resorting to formal and sometimes outdated diplomatic methods. And our experience in one small East Side section, a block perhaps, has led to a next contact, and a next, in widening circles, until our community relationships have come to include the city, the state, the national government, and the world at large. It is rare indeed to find an experienced settlement worker who does not feel kinship with all peoples. In thought and practice we live internationally. In such an atmosphere one cannot feel alien to any people. I was not surprised when a young Negro, wishing to thank me for a kindness, said simply, "You have been a mother to me!" With this security in human kinship astonishing riches are unfolded — old traditions, old arts, and new ideas, brought from other lands by other people.

This story is not to be told impressively in charts and statistics. I cannot tell the story that way any more than could Jacob Riis, who once said to me rather mournfully, after a vain effort to draw up a suitable statement for presentation before a learned group: "I find I don't know how to get statistics. I am like the man in a Western village who, when asked by a research student from the East, 'What is the death rate here?' replied, 'I guess it 's about one death for every person.' "

But if I am not writing a learned treatise, nor an autobiography, neither is this to be an account of persons and events set down merely for the sake of record. My real hope is that I may have the good fortune to encourage people — particularly young people — to participate more widely than they do in the affairs of the going world, with no selfish gain in view beyond increased ability to discuss intelligently or to inquire seriously. The harvest of such living would be a faith in democracy, and an understanding of people that would count against the disastrous currents of indifference and ignorance and prejudice.

Individuals, often negative or apathetic, sometimes only shy, believe that they have no sphere of influence. But there is hardly a person who has not within himself the power to arouse thought or question. An interest in culture and justice, especially if it be accompanied by an effort to further them, constitutes an art of humanity. It is to encourage that art that this book is written.

II

CHANGE COMES TO THE EAST SIDE

LITERATURE has dwelt almost exclusively on the ugly side of our section of New York and scarcely alluded even to the superb bridges. From a point near the House can be seen three of these spans and their towers, as magnificent if not as storied as the bridges of London and Paris. And there are other spots of beauty which vie with any that can be found in the city. Crossing the street from the Settlement and looking to the west, one gazes upon the lofty Woolworth tower, the roofs and masses of the Municipal Buildings, and when the sun is setting the glory of the Lord seems to rest over them. At least that is what a little girl of the neighborhood felt when she said in an awed voice, clasping the hand of a beloved resident, "Miss Knight, does God live there?"

Veering around, one sees to the east a picturesque old church that has stood for more than a hundred years at the corner of Scammel Street, and that still attracts visitors, to look not only at the last slave gallery left in New York City, but also at the diamond scratches "Boss" Tweed made on a windowpane, which the guide exhibits with almost equal pride.   Between the church and the skyscrapers are the problems of society, recording few mutations.   But, now as always, it is fatal to dwell upon the outer symbols of life and poverty, lest one forget the humanity that lives and dies beneath the roofs.   And it is there that the great changes have come.

There is much that has been obvious improvement in the last two decades.   The tragic poems of the Yiddish writer Morris Rosenfeld were true in fact as well as in spirit when they were written.   But the little girl he described in one of them, who never saw the sunlight because she went to work before dawn and toiled till after dark, has gone with as much finality as the East Side boys whom Loring Brace found living in barrels and hidden under tenement stoops.

But one must not forget the picture of the East Side at the turn of the century.   Its story has been told many times, with the accounts of reforms of real social significance that have developed out of compassion for the condition of the people, particularly the little children.   But in the old days, as now, the East Side gave prominent leaders to the dominant political party.   Of them all, ex-Governor Alfred E. Smith is the most dramatic figure, outstanding for the clarity and integrity of his mind and character, his unbroken touch with everyday life and people, and his genius as an administrator.   When I listen to Irving Berlin's haunting music I remember that he lived in the block next us; George Gershwin says he cannot recall in which of the houses in our neighborhood he lived, he moved so often; and when generous Sophie Braslau gives her beautiful voice and art for our entertainments, I remember the doctor, her father, our good neighbor and ally. The Street knew Edward MacDowell in his young boyhood, when the Quakers and their kin possessed the pleasant homes. The little boy who sketched his grandmother's cat so well and whose teacher brought him to us is now recognized in the world of art; frequent on musical and dramatic programmes are the names of girls and boys whom we have known in our clubs and classes. Not a few are listed in the ranks of the literary. Some have been elected to public office, others drafted into the public service because of special knowledge or ability. When I went, not long ago, to consult with one of New York's admired officials, I was moved to say to him, "You 're just as good-looking as you were when I threatened to use a broom to chase you off the front steps because you were too troublesome."

None of the boys we have known has been front-page news because of his gunmanship. And indeed there is no more pitiful reflection than the fact that it takes so little to help the young to grow up with right standards of conduct, so little to prevent the juvenile delinquency which is often the apprenticeship for adult crime.

The condition of the East Side streets has greatly improved, and the grown-ups and children along the sidewalks look spruce, wholesome, and well cared for as compared with those we used to see. As evidence of certain changes in economic status, statistics of the conditions of wage earners, of education, of child health, of delinquency and crime, are elsewhere accessible to students; this is not a compilation of statistics, but a record of human experience. The Russian Revolution was at its beginning most startling in the emergence of great numbers of people, of "the masses," who were spurred to claim rights for themselves. These higher demands have been felt by families as well as by individuals throughout our entire neighborhood. The people whom we know have come to share with multitudes in every land the growing consciousness that they are not "the disinherited," and that they have a right to participate in new standards of comfort and of dignity.

When we went to live on the East Side, one observation that was not difficult to make was that the conventions of our neighbors of foreign birth and of children of the foreign-born differed considerably from American customs. The first mothers' club at the Settlement was made up of eight or nine women of the neighborhood with whom we had become acquainted through the nursing service. When they first met, there was no indication of any experience with social usages, for they came with untidy clothes, safety pins holding together their overflowing blouses; and the talk, interspersed with stories to make instruction palatable, was what might have been given to little children — tales of trick dogs and of hairbreadth escapes from fire, flood, or jungle beast. Last year, the thirty-fifth anniversary of the club produced a gathering of about a hundred women, among them all but one of the original group. This dinner, however, was a meeting of sophisticates, though bobbed hair and occasional evidence of the "beautician's" help did not in the least lessen the emotional warmth, the long reminiscences of what had been and of what they felt they had gained through their association with one another and with the Settlement.

Perhaps I should mention as a highly significant sign of the emancipation of our neighbors from binding tradition the disappearance of the *sheitel*. This was the wig that orthodox Jewish wives had to put on, and that completely hid their own hair. To go on the street without it was legal cause, long ago, for divorce. To-day the young wives in our neighborhood no longer disfigure themselves with the *sheitel* when they appear in public, nor has it been worn by the Jewish immigrants of recent years.

It seems worth while to note here why we place real importance on the elimination of those superficial qualities which are often more divisive than deeper and more fundamental characteristics. Habits consistent with the conventions of other countries, though varying from our own, often mark as "alien" and "queer" people who might otherwise prove to be sympathetic, and sometimes limit the possibilities of real companionship. Granted that manners may be, and often are, insincere and a low standard of valuation, it remains that genuine good manners spring from a true sense of courtesy, based on consideration for the needs and feelings of others. To make the point clear, and to show that we were not

A Grandmother of the East Side

criticizing the ways of another country or group but merely stressing the importance of courtesy, I reminded our first boys' club that "good manners are minor morals," and found as many illustrations as my ingenuity provided. The words have been repeated in the House again and again through the years. Someone has told me it is written that Saint Francis of Assisi used the phrase, but I think neither he nor I plagiarized.

In the beginning of our East Side life, when we went to Albany to press for housing reform or for child protection, we always called those most interested — the mothers — into our council, to ask their views on what evils in their surroundings they would most like to see corrected, and what they felt the remedy should be. Though they were shy, they expressed clearly their abhorrence of dirty tenements, cluttered airshafts and fire escapes, crowded schools, corner saloons, the streets as playgrounds for their children. Now representatives of the women themselves go to Albany, where they most admirably formulate and state their convictions as to needed changes in law or administration. During all this time, while eager to help make a better future for their children, these women, like other groups of the kind, have had a part in social matters beyond their personal interests.

When the Lawrence textile strike stirred the compassionate few who sought the truth and went to Lawrence to get it, these women of their own accord invited the children of the strikers to stay with them, though the hospitality they had to offer was meagre. They sent money for the defense of Sacco and Vanzetti and of Mooney. A most unexpected gift was their contribution to a memorial to Canon Barnett in appreciation of his part in founding the first settlement house, Toynbee Hall, in Whitechapel, London. From their limited treasury they have supported local agencies, particularly the nursing service, of which they tremendously approve, and they have felt a growing responsibility to give voice to their opinions on the issues of the day. With the Settlement influence thus pervading the homes as well as the clubs and classes, it is not surprising when our young people, boys and girls, participate in protest, in resolutions, and in the various methods of registering views that truly express a sense of citizenship.

On the evening of the Fourth of July we have for long years held a celebration on Henry Street. The Edison Company furnishes the illumination, the neighbors hang out flags, the Settlement collects money for the band, and sometimes there is a speaker if one can be found whose voice will carry over these moving crowds. Grown-ups and children dance on the smooth asphalt. There is no discord or need for extra policemen. Some such message as this is usually sent: —

July 4, 1918

President Woodrow Wilson
The White House
Washington, D. C.

Neighbors who have come from many lands are rejoicing together as Americans on Independence Day. From the two street gatherings on Henry Street we send to you, our President, our loyal greetings.

From the dawn of time, children have touched the compassion, the imagination, the protective sense of people, but it is only recently that educators have recognized that adults too have a claim to further development. It is frequently argued that they should not be suffered to remain in a rut, that they should keep pace, at least to some extent, with their often arrogant youngsters. And also there is recognition among all people whose minds are not sealed that with the shortened days and weeks of work the use of increased unemployed time is most important. It is surprisingly easy for men and women who work hard, and who might think that with marriage and parenthood their part in life has been played, to be stirred to consciousness of their value as citizens and as individuals. Settlements have always tried to bring the generations together, as they have tried to bring races and nationalities together, and it has at times required no little manœuvring to awaken the children to pride in their "un-American" parents and to recognition of the gifts they have bestowed. This problem has been much discussed, and it now gains greater significance from the physical fact that there are more older people in the world than there were, that the expectation of life has increased ten years since 1900, and that with greater leisure there is possible a vital contribution on the part of the increased adult population.

On the Feast of Tabernacles in our Jewish neighborhood we set up on our roof a *sukkah* or booth, according to the ritual prescribed in Leviticus for this festival of the "ingathering." The proudest participant in the service is an old man from a neighborhood tenement who chants the religious songs inspired for the occasion hundreds — perhaps thousands — of years ago. The admiration felt for him filters down to the smart young people of the clubs who are invited to the roof; and, after our demonstration of respect for old customs, the neighborhood takes part, bringing fruits and cakes and homemade wine, according to tradition. There is no sense of intrusion, but rather of hospitality, when guests who happen to be at the Settlement, though they know little of Jewish customs, join in the celebration and are moved by the beauty of this ceremony transferred from the Orient to New York's East Side.

Changes in this observance symbolize the changes in the economic condition of the neighborhood. When I first came to the East Side, I would see the pitiful, newly arrived immigrants bargaining with the pushcart dealers for *lulab* (sprays of willow or myrtle) and *esrog* (lemons), the greens and fruit traditionally associated with the festival. Having no place to build the ceremonial booth, as their forbears did, they would lay branches over the roof of the outdoor toilet, which bore a remote suggestion of the traditional *sukkah*. None of to-day's children know of this sorry makeshift, and their reintroduction to the old customs of the festival comes from people who see the spiritual message and who love to have the beautiful preserved as an inheritance.

When the settlements wish to give an exhibition of ancient and modern art they can draw upon their neighbors for beautiful old bits. Lace, embroidery, pottery, carvings, jewelry, are treasured as reminders of the old home. The young people are only now beginning to appreciate these heirlooms. "Hundred per cent Americanism" had led to a contemptuous feeling even toward these. Some of the treasures given to me long ago by immigrants I have now passed over to their grandchildren. In truth, I cannot say that they always value them as I did.

The beautiful brasses and coppers that have delighted the hearts of many collectors and made Allen Street famous have been given away with great liberality. But few know that the seven-branched candlestick that stands on so many non-Jewish tables symbolizes the seven planets and the Sabbath prayer through which God unites all.

Hospitality is a tradition in our neighborhood. One of the invitations most prized at Henry Street is that which bids us welcome to a Passover service. Despite the influences of liberalism within the faith, and scorn on the part of some of those who have broken with old traditions, it remains an impressive and a lovely ceremonial. So generous are the homes, even those with the fewest dollars, that homemade wine, an essential part of the Passover observance, is pressed upon acquaintances who are not of the faith, and sometimes unwisely. Our colored janitor once came to my door obviously under the influence of liquor. When I ventured to reprove him he said, speaking in the accents of one who has drunk too deeply, "Don' you worry — ish all ri' — ish holy Jewish wine."

Our neighbors share their old-country customs and

skills not only with the Settlement but with one another. At a woman's club composed of different nationalities, an Italian housewife brought to the meeting a fragrant dish of spaghetti to show how the popular dish of her homeland should be cooked and eaten. This inspired a Russian Jewess to bring her *gefüllte Fisch*, most difficult to prepare and highly esteemed by true believers.

Needless to say, we are always sympathetic to the cause of the workers. Their arguments are generally sound, and only a blind spot could make one fail to realize how wise it is to help forward the organization of the wage earners as a direct road toward making relief unnecessary, and toward enabling them to learn to take the responsibility for their work conditions and their family needs.

The quick response of at least one person to whom this philosophy was presented is a good illustration of the validity of the point of view. In many ways Jacob H. Schiff was one of the clearest-minded as well as one of the most generous of American citizens, and the Settlement owes an unpayable debt to him and to his family. In one of our frequent conferences on social conditions and wise relief, I told him the story of some needleworkers in our neighborhood and their impending strike. I explained that because the busy season for the trade was beginning they would have to make terms quickly or accept a poor bargain for their labor. This sympathetic man used the same method in dealing with social questions that he did in his business organization.

He marked the statement that the men could not support themselves and their families on the wages paid them, and immediately expressed a desire to participate in some steps for resolving the situation. A conference at the Settlement was suggested, to which I promised to bring representatives of the workers and the middlemen if he would bring spokesmen for the employers.

During the meeting one of the latter group said: "This meeting will take us nowhere. The whole problem comes down to a question of supply and demand. I may be forced to pay so little for the work out of one pocket that I shall have to help with relief from my charity pocket."

Mr. Schiff, shocked by this statement before the poverty-stricken and earnest workers, left the conference. He asked for direction as to what practical help he could give. He did not turn money over to the union, but he authorized my greatly prized fellow worker, Lavinia Dock, and me to give such help as was needed. Every morning we went to strike headquarters to learn the urgent needs of the families involved. At the end of the day we sent a statement to our friend, itemizing the rent paid, the food provided, the coal supplied, and he promptly paid the bills. When the dispute was settled to the advantage of the workers, no one was more gratified than this good man, who said, with the workers, "We won that strike."

The unspeakable tenement sweatshops of which many, like myself, have written have disappeared. We no longer encounter these home factories in which we used to share such horrors as the delivery of a baby just before the coming of the workers to set their machines for

the day's toil. These conditions would not be tolerated to-day by the people themselves; enlightened leaders
among the workers have taken the responsibility of
arousing this consciousness of the elementary rights of
men and women.

In my earlier days on the East Side, labor unions were
feared as Socialists were later and as Communists are
to-day. I remember telling at a dinner of comfortable
people — bankers, industrialists, a lawyer or two —
about one of these heroic labor leaders. Every knife
and fork stopped when I mentioned casually that I knew
and respected a "walking delegate." I went on to speak
of a man who had organized the cloak makers in one
of their early protests against the lot of the sweated
workers. I still remember that faces sobered as I told
about this leader and his struggle. Of course, it was
important for him to make a good appearance when
he met employers. He was a tall, fine-looking man,
and quite impressive, but his own straits were pitiful.
His wife washed and starched and ironed his shirt — his
only shirt — each night so that he might look well the
next day. It was a joy to me to have any part in
helping him. But these friends of mine — "capitalists,"
as he and his comrades would have lumped them — were
not at all sympathetic when I told the story. They said
I had "gone over to the other side." Such lack of
understanding and interest would not be encountered
to-day in any group that could lay claim to intelligence.

At the time of the Lawrence strike, when feeling ran
high on both sides, a meeting at the House heard first-
hand reports of the situation. At once there was
criticism. The Settlement was being used for propa-

ganda! What had support of a struggle for wages and factory conditions to do with social work? To-day concern with industrial conditions in a social programme is taken as a matter of course. Indeed, unconsciousness of the relationship between seasonal irregularity in industry, laxity in the labor law or its enforcement, wage levels, hours of work, and the family situation of industrial workers would be considered evidence of almost unbelievable shortsightedness. In the programme of the National Conference of Social Work, the large place given to industrial conditions and their significance testifies to the awareness on the part of social workers of the influence of business and industry on the whole range of their responsibilities, including unemployment relief, child welfare, character building, public health, juvenile delinquency, and so on — almost without end.

A social geologist would find in the Henry Street neighborhood the strata of many civilizations, and of late there has been added a group of colored people.

Over five years ago we observed an increase in the number of Negroes in our streets, and our interest soon led us to find a colony living in wretched homes — many unfit for anyone to live in — a few blocks from the Settlement. The story ran that the owner of these houses discovered that a laundress uptown was a leader among her people, and he made it advantageous to her to bring tenants to his lower East Side properties.

Though the differences among these three hundred people are not obvious, they represent many backgrounds. There are families from Jamaica, from the Virgin Islands, "Gullahs" from the coast of South

MILLIE

A HENRY STREET FAVORITE

Carolina, field hands and house servants from Virginia, Georgia, and Alabama, Liberians — it is said there are fifteen different origins.

At Henry Street it is a long time since we had any fear of embarrassment over the typically American "race problem," because distinguished colored people are so often our guests — poets, writers of fiction, musicians, some engaged in efforts for the betterment of their race. Guests of other races who come for lunch or dinner accept our social point of view. Residents have something to say about additions to the family, but only one registered a negative vote against accepting a young Negro woman, a graduate of Oberlin doing postgraduate work at Bryn Mawr, who during vacation wanted to study the new group of colored people in our neighborhood. Though she might easily have "passed," she had no desire to do so. When the subject was discussed she said, "I do not blame my people who 'pass'; they suffer so much because of their race. But I would not do it, for I should lose more than I should gain."

That, I find, is not an uncommon conviction on the part of the highly educated, sensitive men and women of the race. And they enjoy, as we enjoy, the humors of the primitives. The coming of the Negro colony to our neighborhood has often given us very rare delights.

These new neighbors were the special interest of two residents, husband and wife, and their sympathy, friendship, and love of humor were richly rewarded.

The colored man who took care of our furnace for many years, and who was truly religious, called on us at frequent intervals for coöperation in organizing a congregation. We were willing helpers, contributing the loan of folding chairs and tables, giving at one time two dollars to buy an organ from the Salvation Army, and often turning over the gymnasium for "affairs" to raise money for the impecunious parish. The arrival of the "visiting clergy" who came to preach at Frederick's church from time to time was always an event. When one, a bricklayer by day, was asked whether he had a church, he answered promptly, "No, ma'am, I 'se ecclesiastical an' loose."

Frederick's congregation first met in a little old store, with dingy paper hanging in strips from the walls. After the place had been cleaned, in preparation for the first service, Frederick arranged for a loan of Henry Street sheets to drape the tattered walls. His opening remarks at that first service have never been forgotten: —

"Bretheren an' Sisters, dis am jus' a simple church meetinghouse, but we never would 'a' had this if it had n't a been for the Settlement, which is our bes' frien'. But it 's ours, an' I 'se glad to see you-all here. I did n't ask the President of the United States to come, fer he would n't 'a' come.   I did n't ask the Governor of New York to come, fer he would n't 'a' come.   I did n't ask the Mayor [Jimmy Walker] to come, fer he 's busy wid udder t'ings. But I did ask Jesus to come, an' He 's here."

Frederick once preached a sermon that had a practical as well as a spiritual application: —

"Bretheren an' Sisters, we is joined together to help

each other.   That 's what we oughta do an' that 's what
we 're goin' to do, but we must do it in de right way.
When I lived in Harlem, me an' two other deacons felt
de call to help an errin' sister.   We wrote to her an'
we said, 'Come back to us an' we will help you lead
a good life.   Take care o' your husban' an' leave dat
other woman's hus-  ban' alone.'   Two
days later I got a
paper.   It was a
subpœna, an' I was
sued for seventy-five
thousand dollars fer
defilation o' charac-
ter.   I wen' to co't
an' there sat the
judge, an' he says to
me, 'How so come
you call yo'self Rev-
erend?   What col-
lege you graduate
frum?'   An' I say,
'Oh, yo' honor, I
graduate frum de
Knee College.'   An' he says, 'Never hear o' dat college.'   So I git right down dere in co't an' I showed
him what de Knee College was.   An' I prayed to de
Lawd to help de President an' de judge an' all de white
people an' all de black people, an' help me help dem.
De judge he turn to Susan an' her friends an' he say,
'Looky here, I don't think he means defile you.'   An'

he says to me, 'That's right, Frederick; do everything what you kin to help yo' people, but don' you nevermo' write it.' "

One Christmas night I stopped at the parish house of All Saints Church on Henry Street to leave a message of the season for the rector. I was directed to the church, next door, and found him conducting the Mass. As I sat in a pew I could not help pondering on the fact that behind me, under the roof, was the slave gallery left from the days when Henry Street was "stylish" and its houses the homes of the rich, and that the slaves in that black hole could not have been comfortable physically while they received the word of the spirit from the pulpit far below. But, while I could not have seen the slave gallery without turning my head, I could see among the congregation many West Indians who by their genuflections and their familiarity with the service not only showed their acquaintance with High Church Episcopal ritual, but indicated that they were entirely at home in the pews. The choir was made up of both black and white members, nearly all trained in the Settlement music school.

Ever since the suffrage fight was won, and "votes for women" became an unexciting and accepted fact, we have heard less and less about "equal rights for women" in nonpolitical aspects of life. Perhaps one reason is that it is easier for women and girls in industry to insist on their "rights" since the Women's Trade Union League was organized, and developed under the leadership of Mary E. Dreier and Rose Schneiderman and the support of such courageous spirits as Mrs. Franklin D. Roosevelt.

Long ago, before the League existed, I tried in one strike to secure equal rights for women and girls employed in shops, and for many years I held sixteen dollars as dues that in the first flush of strike victory the girls had paid me, their treasurer. But the question was not vital, for girls' work at that time was considered merely an interlude between school and early marriage. Times have changed, and while women need not give so much of their energy to acquiring rights as women, there is a growing need for them to throw their strength into the struggle for the rights of workers. Perhaps there are still some technical handicaps, but these are bound to be swept away when there is established an awareness of the privilege of work and the necessity of working under desirable conditions. This, of course, was more true of the decade before the depression than it has been of the last few years. But I think a lesson has been learned and the leaders of neighborhood groups and other social workers will be more free to stand with men and women workers for principles and for organizing intelligent public opinion behind them rather than to hire halls and help in their struggle for purely material gains.

Years ago a topical singer on the roof of Clinton Hall (a building erected through the Settlement to afford a proper meeting place for the trade-unions and for weddings) recorded the saga of a workingman who had prospered and reached the high estate of a cigar and a piano in the house. There are many pianos now in the houses. The music schools of the various settlements give evidence of the extraordinarily high standards that are set. The pupils pay for instruction when they are able, and overburdened mothers can and do join classes in music appreciation because they want to understand what their children are learning. The chamber music programmes in our Little Theatre by such organizations as the Musical Art, the Gordon, and the Stradivarius Quartettes, and other equally distinguished artists, draw understanding audiences, and always the performers have expressed their gratification because of the obvious appreciation with which their best was greeted.

The radio has been an ally in bringing good music to multitudes. A cobbler recently explained his tardiness in coming from his little back room to the front shop by saying that he had been listening to the Damrosch programme; he had not wanted to miss it, as he had heard them all, "and they are beautiful."

The gayety, the humor, and the happy home life frequently found under hard conditions have not changed with the many changes in our neighborhood. In a shabby, tumbling wooden house near us live a deserted wife and her three boys. The father has established another household, and his earnings are divided between the two families. Despite the danger of the roof falling in, the rooms are always scrupulously clean, and some treasures from Bohemia that the mother has preserved give color and atmosphere. The eldest son, now twelve years old, takes the responsibility of protector, tender with his mother, careful of his two brothers. The sweetness of that home and the fineness of the lives lived there can scarcely be exaggerated.

Years ago the appearance of a carriage in our block was exciting to the children, and we would be met long before we reached our door by eager youngsters clamoring to know, "Who 's got a wedding by you?" Such luxury was unheard of except at a wedding or a funeral. To-day taxis are easily accessible. On reunion nights the privately owned cars are numerous, and not even the least experienced in a worldly sense is astonished at any visitor, for it is taken for granted that, with to-day's transportation facilities, strangers will find their way from other parts of the city to our quarter. Indeed, with the broad, well-paved, new streets that have followed the use of the automobile, bankers, lawyers, and other busy people pass daily from their uptown homes to their downtown offices and banks. This has the important effect of unifying the extremes of the city, and the lower East Side is no longer an unknown and foreign land to these citizens.

The newsboys' lodging house, once a serious problem, has long since disappeared from our immediate vicinity. The mothers themselves objected to this "hang-out" as one which provided an easy excuse for staying away from home. They helped bring about its removal, as they have helped put an end to street selling by the tiny children who used to be sent out as news vendors because their still-babyish charm and appeal often moved people to buy their papers and to give them odd pennies.

Another great change is the value placed on country holidays. The children themselves, at departure for their two weeks of "Fresh Air," present an entirely different picture from the companies of earlier days. No

longer do newspapers hold the vacation wardrobe.   It
is hardly necessary for us to furnish the tidy canvas
clothes bags we long ago devised.   I marveled one day
when I went to the lobby where the children were assembled to see the neat suitcases and the efficient tag-
ging of each piece of luggage.   Who would have
dreamed of this in the days when we carried the clumsy
newspaper bundles, praying fervently that the break
would not come at any rate till we were seated in the
train?

Some of our Settlement athletics have developed conspicuous stars, and there have been times when we could
boast of a pugilist or two.   It is clearly understood that
we are not all highbrow or arty, not always politically
conscious or striving for a Ph.D.

Though our neighborhood has felt the heaviest burden
of the depression, we also had our part in the "boom."
In that period, which now seems so remote, we witnessed in our neighborhood an epidemic of gambling reminding one of the South Sea Bubble stories.   Even the
pushcart peddlers and the scrubwomen caught the get-
rich-quick fever that burned so high in Wall Street, and
speculated in small fractions of shares of stock.   One
would hear a boast of the "rise" in Blue Cat Oil, in
which the speaker held two tenths of a share, and the
details of the "deal" in which another had secured a
twelfth of a share of Universal Radio.   But, if the
operations were minute, the losses when the bubble
burst were easier to bear philosophically than those of
some New Yorkers who "lost everything" because they
had had the means to play for bigger stakes.

The tragedy of unemployment has hit us hard. Pitiful indeed is the realization that many of our neighbors are not inclined to tell us of their desperate plight and their need of work. But they are sympathetic to each other; they try to find jobs for one another and show the same old compassion of the needy for the needy that is so naturally comprehended and accepted because with it comes the leveling thought, "I 've been through it, too." We have seldom used the word "poor." It rarely appears in this book. To us it is a "weasel word," conveying a sense of failure most humiliating to the people who suffer from poverty.

In spite of the hard times, there are many "empties" in our neighborhood, because, as standards of living have been lifted, the uncrushable desire for a bathroom has increased, and the people have moved away in quest of modern conveniences — and in some instances to avoid the rats! But they come back to see us, to keep alive their friendships, and for old sake's sake, and there are most happy reunions on Henry Street. I hardly think that alumni of any college, even a college where "old grads" dress up most elaborately to proclaim their class affiliations, exhibit more pleasure or more enthusiasm than do the home-comers to the Settlement.

At the celebration of the Fortieth Anniversary of the House, a radio broadcaster, without mentioning names, retold a story I had somewhere told of the nurse's visit I paid to a household that stirred me to come to the East Side. Two days later the broadcaster courteously sent me the correspondence which had come to him as a result of that talk. Among the letters was a note

which read, with a ring of pride between the lines,
"I'd like you to know that I am the case you talked
about yesterday when you told about Miss Wald."

I am sorry to say that the least improvement I can
chronicle is in housing, though inside the homes things
are ever so much better than they used to be.   That the
people themselves are refusing to submit to unwhole-
someness and inconvenience was shown in a recent
survey by the East Side Chamber of Commerce, which
revealed that four out of five vacant apartments have
no central heat, three out of five have no baths and have
water-closets in the hall to be shared by several families.
Such facts prove how far behind modern standards is
the housing condition of the small wage earner.

More than thirty years ago we felt the urgent need to
instill in the people themselves a desire for better homes.
I went to Europe one summer holding an option at a
bargain price on a most desirable property that faced
the river.   In urging capitalists to help provide decent
housing on a paying basis ("Christianity at 5 per cent"
it was called), we tried to impress upon them the value
to the people themselves of adequate, dignified homes
for growing children, and the great advantage to the
workingman of being able to walk to work.   Good
housing in our neighborhood, we argued, would save the
small wage earner the cost of transportation, relieve
to some extent the congested cars, and gain for recreation and for family life the two and sometimes three
hours required for wearisome travel.   This water-front
project never materialized, but we do have one shining
example of what housing in our neighborhood might be,

and some day must be, in the beautiful structure that
now covers the site for a hundred years occupied by the
Hoe Manufacturing Company.

The old factory was long an ugly landmark in the
community. From its windows some years since the
uncouth workers threw stones and insults on the solemn
procession of marching men who followed afoot the
coffin of a chief rabbi. The only reason for the atrocious behavior probably was that the funeral without
carriages, and the dark men, many of them bearded,
seemed to these American factory workers "foreign"
and "queer." Now, taking the place of the old factory
are beautiful dwellings, — none more convenient or
better planned on Park Avenue, — built because of the
social conviction of Governor Herbert Lehman and
Aaron Rabinowitz, one of "our" boys, now a member of
the State Housing Board, who generously attribute their
impulse to the Settlement influences. The apartments
are coöperative in ownership. They are under the wise
management of the Amalgamated Clothing Workers of
America, of which Sidney Hillman is the head and the
guiding force. And, though the generosity of those
responsible for the undertaking is great, it is a pleasure
to know that, whereas landlords generally have suffered
throughout the city in recent years, the backers of this
model housing project were satisfied with the returns on
their investment even in the terrible winter of 1932–
1933.

In the planning of these dwellings, beauty and health
were both recognized, and no small part of the capital
was invested in developing the plantation within the

courts, in the purchase of soil and the skilled gardening, that grass and shrubbery and flowers might grow worthily. Every room fronts either on this green oasis or on the street. There are no rooms shut off from sunlight and air. Consciousness of what would serve to simplify the lives of the tenants, particularly the mothers, is shown in a thousand details — none, perhaps, more ingenious than the "baby-carriage garage," reached by a short ramp from the courtyard, where these necessary vehicles may be safely and conveniently kept without encroaching on apartments, halls, or elevators. The artisans showed their interest in the purpose of the building by contributing lovely bits, a fountain on the roof, special ornamental tiling, and so on.

To-day the thoughts of many people have been turned toward the advantages of good housing on a large scale, stirred not only by consciousness of the social values involved, but also by the possibility of starting the wheels of industry. Here is a great opportunity, but one that calls for wisdom and insight. In New York City, Christie and Forsythe Streets are monuments to the futility of omitting business sense and social experience not only from a housing scheme but from any plan for public betterment. Here the city spent $5,000,000 for a site for a model housing development which to-day presents almost insuperable obstacles to such use. A narrow strip, lying between two main traffic arteries, it is suitable for a parkway, but not for desirable dwellings. It was taken over, needless to say, without adequate consultation with social workers or housing experts. To-day the notorious "lung block," the area that acquired its name from the high incidence of tuberculosis developed there, has been abolished to give place to a very desirable housing unit made possible through a Reconstruction Finance Corporation loan to a commercial builder, who has already transformed the extreme eastern parts of hitherto undesirable property in the Forties.

But only large investment can clear the section, for not even a new house can be attractive unless its environment is good. Such projects as the Amalgamated Cooperatives and the new scheme for the "lung block," valuable as they are, do not meet the needs of the people of the lowest economic resources. The tenements they now live in are unfit for human habitation, despite the good housekeeping of many a mother. It is not likely that provision for them would ever pay interest on the investment, and, unless something more self-respecting is developed, "charity" would have to issue the invitation to live in the new house.

How soon, with changing concepts of social responsibility, we shall come to subsidized apartments, or to government-owned and noncommercial houses, is a conjecture. Numerous groups are giving their best thought to the problem, the most urgent change needed on the East Side, as in so many similar areas of our American cities; and there is reason to hope that we may live to see the day when we shall not be shamed by the "homes" where so many of the men and women of to-morrow are spending their childhood and youth.

III

PEOPLE WHO HAVE CROSSED OUR THRESHOLD

THIS chapter can be of only modest proportion; perhaps it would never have been included if it did not seem to carry a message that visitors sense in the House itself. Hospitality, if it be true, knows not the barriers of convention and is not a studied expression, but evolves out of respect for people and for their importance as human beings. It seems to be essential that centres of friendliness to people and to causes should be available, that the doors should swing open without hindrance and the voices reach ears that will hear. This cannot be accomplished if propaganda, the desire to make all people think one way, influences the place. The House on Henry Street does not differ from similar households, and because the settlement is flexible, shaped by people of conviction and broad contacts, its use is as varied as the individuals who make up the circle.

There has been through the years a procession across our threshold — those who have become part of the very texture of the House and those who have tarried but a little while, those who have come from far-away lands and those who have come because word had reached them that they might find in this place help and surely sympathy. We have had a continuity of family life, developing a fellowship rich beyond description or appraisal. Varied are the occupations of the residents, though the first requirement for eligibility is not the candidate's vocation, but his interest in social progress and his participation, at least to some degree, in efforts in that direction. And of course a sense of humor.

Through this book I tell of the neighbors, and of the particular problems and sometimes the special joys that have brought them to their friends. But there are happy memories of other people who have crossed our threshold, whose coming has enriched our understanding, and I trust I may be forgiven if the temptation is sometimes irresistible to add treasured details until the mention of a friend has grown to the proportions of a character sketch.

I think all who know the Settlement will comprehend why the one who has first place in our processional is Florence Kelley. For twenty-five years she was an inspiration to us and often a prod, but she was always brilliant, even at the breakfast table. It will be a sad loss to America if the story of that ardent crusader is not retold to coming generations, for her times knew none more effective. She made her generation think! She goaded others with the whips of her wit, her quickness, her bottomless sympathy, her readiness to act wherever new danger menaced the child or the people whom she believed were imposed upon by outdated legislation or other discriminations. She was responsible for great "ethical gains" through legislation. From her college days to the end of her life her brilliant mind turned toward amelioration of social conditions, but it never paused there. She urged us to work for the abolition of poverty. Her wit made people remember the sober things she said.

She was one of the first members of the Socialist Party in this country. Her translation of Engels fixed her in that fellowship. But the Socialist Party of the early days bore little relationship to its present organization under the guidance of Norman Thomas. Long ago, as we stood by the window watching a poor little procession carrying the banner of Socialism, Mrs. Kelley said, "I belong there, but they put me out because I could speak English."

She was intolerant of superficiality, of selfishness, of inaction, and her tongue could be very sharp. Once I was trying to apologize for a woman who had disappointed those who had expected much of her, saying, "Well, she has an open mind." "That's what I object to," flashed Florence Kelley. "It's open top and bottom."

Her spirits were often youthful to the point of mischievousness. One day I was presiding over a very serious meeting, conscious of my inability to meet the requirements of the occasion. Before me sat a woman suffering from bad boils and bandaged as such afflictions require; near her were a man with troublesome eyes and another with a conspicuously bald head and oddly trimmed beard. These three were very much in view from the chairman's seat. When Florence Kelley bent over confidentially, I thought of course it was to offer me a helpful suggestion as to procedure. Instead, she completely upset the presiding officer by whispering, "Do you remember what the lady said at the zoo when she saw the hippos — 'My, ain't they plain!' "

Newton D. Baker, long the president of the National Consumers' League, of which Mrs. Kelley was general secretary, said that he never left her presence without feeling that his own flagging spirit and energies had been "reinspired by the touch of elemental force."

During this period of the New Deal it is pleasing to know how many who have been what we call "Henry Streeters" are helping shape social legislation. Governor Lehman in Albany has given the State of New York a markedly effective administration. Since his college days he has devoted himself with unstinted generosity to causes, and in his elective office has demonstrated the importance of trained intelligence and social vision in the great affairs of the state. The Henry Morgenthaus, both Sr. and Jr., Adolf A. Berle, Jr., and many others are translating their training and experience and convictions into measures which promise a better life — at least a more secure life.

My friend Robert Wagner, United States Senator

from New York and effective champion of sound labor legislation, recently said: "Legislators, no matter how ardent their desire for public service, have frequently been so busy during their earlier years with the routine work of a profession that they have lacked the time to become fully aware of the facts and principles of social work. Because of this, one could not overestimate the central part played by social workers in bringing before their representatives in Congress and state legislatures the present and insistent problems of modern-day life."

What the settlement-house experience has often meant was finely stated by Ernest Poole: "Here — when I was still a youngster, thank God — I came into a personal intimate home with windows looking all over the world. And I come here again and again and again."

There is pride in remembering that when Sidney Hillman came to New York, little known outside the particular group of factory workers with whom he had thrown his lot, he knocked at our door and asked if there was room for one more. There are many people in this and in other countries who now recognize the vision and the truly statesmanlike qualities of this labor leader. When Seebohm Rowntree, the English industrialist, was in New York he expressed his disappointment that organized labor here was not actively engaged in promoting better conditions, but added: "Sidney Hillman is a figure apart. There is none more distinguished anywhere." Among Sidney Hillman's achievements, in addition to the coöperative housing projects of the Amalgamated Clothing Workers, are the joint employer-employee research programme of this great labor union, its labor bank, its pioneer unemployment insurance scheme, and its active workers' education. His is the steady hand that holds the union together, while his fine mind creates the practical plan for a more abundant life.

One evening years ago, in the little back garden of the main house when the whole family was gathered for after-dinner coffee, this creative thinker, looking worn from the trials of the day, taking only a few moments' respite before the evening activities, said: "I am not interested in higher wages or shorter hours of work as ends in themselves. What would higher wages and shorter hours avail if the workers did not know how to use their lives to develop their own qualities and help build up a better society?" He has been criticized, at times persecuted, for his determination to carry out this programme, which he believes can only come about through coöperative effort on the part of the working population. His influence is not limited to workers in the needle trades. Those who are aware of the origins of farseeing legislative measures are never surprised when they discover the guidance of Sidney Hillman.

Elizabeth Farrell, to whose work I refer elsewhere, lived on Henry Street for many years. She contributed the original project, truly scientific as well as humanitarian, for the education of the retarded child in the public school system.

Lavinia Dock, pioneer nurse, pioneer suffragist, has shared in almost countless measures that have increased the nurse's education and opportunities. An educator herself, her *Materia Medica* has gone through repeated editions, and the history of nursing which she and Miss Nutting prepared is a classic. But this represents only one segment of her interest. I cannot even say it was always the dominant interest, for the rights of women have been well to the fore. In her years with us, everyone admired her, none feared her, though she was sometimes very fierce in her denunciations. Reputed a manhater, we knew her as a lover of mankind. Though a pacifist, she believed in militant suffrage, and one eventful election day, when women in New York were appropriating the tactics of the English suffragettes, the captain of our precinct came in after the polls closed and very repentantly asked me to apologize for him to Lavinia Dock, whom he greatly admired. "For," said Captain Handy, "I could n't arrest her, I just could n't do it, and I know that was what she wanted."

It would be unprofitable to select from the group only the individuals whose names are most widely known, because many of the outstanding participants in the settlement adventure have worked quietly. Generous Felix Warburg, Charles C. Burlingham, friend of all just causes, Governor Lehman, former Governor Smith, George W. Alger, and their distinguished colleagues on the Settlement Board of Directors, give of their best that the Settlement venture may be exploited to its utmost. But another board member, Hyman Schroeder, has been one of us since at eleven he joined the first boys' club. His quick comprehension and sympathy have never been dulled by repetition of claims and appeals.   He seems to have made of his early obstacles a finer-tempered tool of service.

At Residents' Meeting distinguished authorities on subjects of the day find reënforcement, they say, in the frank criticism and the development of discussion based on actual day-by-day contact of the settlement people with the life around them, often in contrast with their own theoretical approach.

Sometimes, as was the case with Madame Naidu, the distinguished associate of Gandhi, there is sharp argument.   Madame Naidu was ready to inform our group on Indian criticism of the British Government, to explain her countrymen's objectives and their outlook.   I fear she almost lost her temper (if indeed she did not entirely do so) because the questions that followed her presentation showed what was to her an inexcusable ignorance of the details of Anglo-Indian politics.   She smarted, too, because in her judgment there was not sufficient protest in America against Katherine Mayo's book.   She repeated Gandhi's comment on *Mother India* — that it was "true, but not the truth."   Tagore and Madame Suradji and thoroughgoing Englishmen have been among many who have tried to keep our household abreast of India's problem.

Tagore, a tremendously impressive figure, read his poems for us in the Little Theatre and then came to the House for tea.   As he walked along Henry Street with his flowing gray robe and long beard, a little girl tugged at my skirt and whispered, "Oh, Miss Wald, is that God?"

"No," I answered, "but he is a great friend of His."

At tea, when I told our distinguished guest that the children had mistaken him for God, there was no dissent — he accepted the tribute.

The Zionists, the Arabs, and the British have discussed frankly their views of the situation in Palestine, and have sometimes been in surprising agreement on fundamental points at issue.

Though I was obliged to withdraw from active membership in the National Association for the Advancement of Colored People, Mrs. Kelley represented the Settlement as well as herself by her participation. At the time of the first convention of the organization, formed to further better race relations in this country, the occasion promised to be almost too serious unless some social provision were made. I suggested a party at the House, but even the organizing committee was fearful.

"Oh, no!" they protested. "It won't do! As soon as white and colored people sit down and eat together there begin to be newspaper stories about social equality."

"But two hundred members of the conference could n't sit down," I submitted. "Our house is too small. Everybody would have to stand up for supper."

"Then it would be all right," they said with relief, and the party was successful.

I was much moved when I contrasted the first timid conference with the superb meeting in Washington in 1932. On Sunday evening the auditorium of the beautiful Labor Building was devoted to a memorial to Florence Kelley. The anxious misgivings of the first

meeting were things of the past, and this was a truly
glorious occasion, organized by educated leaders of the
Negro race.   Society has built up artificial barriers, and,
like the Walls of Jericho, we find that they tumble
when the trumpets are loud and clear enough and the
marchers persevere to the seventh round.

The House solved a dilemma for our colored friends
when Mrs. Cobden-Sanderson was our guest.   The
Negro intelligentsia had never forgotten that her father
befriended their fathers during the Civil War.   They
wished to give a reception for Mrs. Cobden-Sanderson,
but there was no public place they could secure at that
time which seemed dignified enough for this distinguished lady.   We gave the Settlement's beautiful
dining room and the residents' sitting room for their
hospitality, and we were their guests.

Among our summer residents are often students and
teachers from the South who come North to get settlement experience.   In residence one summer was a Negro
girl who, as I have said, had graduated from Oberlin and
was taking postgraduate study at Bryn Mawr.   At the
end of the season I asked a young man, a teacher in a
Southern college, what had been his most interesting
experience while he was with us.   He seemed uncertain,
and I suggested that living in the house with a colored
person on an equal footing and eating at the same table
must have seemed unusual.   Said the young man, "I
forgot she was a Negro."

I cannot refrain from including in this chapter the
story of Peter Caulfield, a tramp whose visits to us were
not frequent, though I knew him for many years, but

whose personality fixed him in my memory. When first we met, Peter was not quite twenty — thin, tall, and consumptive. One of our nurses, caring for a woman in a poor tenement, introduced us. Peter had knocked at the door of the tenement to ask for food. To see an American boy begging in our neighborhood was unusual. The nurse asked him why he came there. "Where would I go when I was hungry if not to the poor?" said Peter.

The nurse gave him a scrap of paper with my name and address on it, and he found his way to Henry Street. Somewhat diffident he seemed, and very thinly clad. He said he was a waiter by trade, and that he spent the winters in the South and the summers in the North. He had been ill in the hospital, and so had lost the chance of going South that year. "When you hang underneath a car where there's no chance of a brakie going through, you have to think of the weather," he said.

Peter seemed so unfit to struggle through a winter of unemployment that I offered to send him to a farm in Dutchess County. "To make quite sure," I said, "I shall have to write and find out whether they can take you. And I have to be certain you can get along without drink, for you will not get it there."

"Can I have hot coffee sometimes?" he wanted to know. "And hot tea? And hot soup?"

I felt safe in promising this.

"Then I won't need drink."

While he waited for a reply to my letter, Peter was boarded at a cheap temperance place in the neighborhood. He called every day, fairly clean and brushed.

One day he came smelling of liquor. I said, "I'm not trying to reform you, Peter, but please don't let me waste money on railroad fare if you are dependent on liquor."

Peter explained: "I minded a wagon for a man in the Bowery and he treated me. I could n't say, 'Give me a glass of milk instead.' How would that have looked?"

In a few days Peter went to the farm. I had occasional letters from him. At Easter I sent him a card of the season. A few days later he rushed in, looking well fed and wholesome. His story (and it was a true one) was that there had been a fire the night before, and the director of the farm had given the men and boys placed with him money to get back to New York. Spring had come and he thought they could fend for themselves. Peter showed with pride the Easter card and said, "Nothing happened to this."

He would not take money from me and I was obliged to throw a coin after him down the stairs.

Peter called regularly on his return from the South, and again in the fall before his departure, and gave me minute details of how to travel without a ticket.

One day a friend of mine, a member of the House of Morgan, called to say good-bye. He was leaving in a private car for St. Augustine. Peter called twenty minutes later. He too was going to St. Augustine. I like to think they went on the same train. One friend wrote telling of his fine journey, the luxurious appointments, the care that had been taken to make every detail agreeable. The other friend wrote: "I got here OK. Good car. I like this place, but for business give me New York. I hope you will send me a letter to the post office. It is the custom of this place to go to the post office for the mail."

Peter called one New Year's Eve — alas, the worse for drink. We were preparing for a musical, and when I hurried down to the basement, there stood poor Peter, ashamed. I said, "You came to wish me a happy New Year, did you? How kind of you, Peter!"

"No," said Peter, "I went to the hospital again and I was too late to go South. But I could n't bear to sleep in a park on New Year's Eve. It would n't be lucky, and I thought you would find a place for me somewhere."

On another occasion a most unpleasing tramp came to Henry Street, asked for me, and stated his needs. I felt that he was in some way connected with Peter, and I was sorry that Peter should have sent him. The next time I saw him I told him of this mendicant, and said: "You know, you and I are friends, but I don't want you to send people like that man to me, and I am surprised that you did."

Peter at once identified the tramp. "Was that the fellow?" he demanded, and when I recognized the description he burst out, "Well, what do you know about that! The big skunk! Why, you know, Miss Wald, I don't talk about you to anyone. I would n't send anyone like that to you. I hope you did n't give him nothing. [I did n't.] Here 's how it was. We was laying out under the trees, one night in Wyoming last summer. He got to talking about his home and his mother and all that. And I — well, I guess I got kind of soft, and I talked about you and how good you 've been to me.   And then — well, the big slob!"

Some time later the chaplain from the Tombs came to see me to ask whether I would befriend a prisoner who had been there many months and who said I knew him.   His name was Peter Caulfield.   I went at once to the prison, but the hour was too late to see him.   A message by the guard asked whether he had a lawyer. The answer came back, scrawled on the margin of a newspaper: "My lawyer is Miss Lillian D. Wald."

Through the District Attorney I learned that Peter had been arrested for stealing a roll of towels.   Peter's story was told, his unfitness for work, and I added that he made an effort to take care of himself.   I had never known Peter to lie or to steal.   I promised that if ever Peter were released I would protect the city from his dangerous presence by sending him to the country. Alas, I was subpœnaed to appear in court.   There before the judge stood this poor creature.   He might have been the very man described by Tolstoy.   His Adam's apple worked up and down with embarrassment and he did not look at the witness.   The judge dismissed him.   When I reached the Settlement, Peter had appeared and gone.   He must have run all the way. He had come to the door only to say he wanted to thank me for what I had done for him, and then vanished.

It was not long after this that I received a letter: —

Deer Frend — I guess I got to face the music this time. Id like to say good bye, and Id like to say Im sorry I came to your house that New Years night when Id had a drink.

Next day found me at the hospital. Peter was obviously about to "face the music." "Peter," I said, "despite your ways there is so much that is good about you I am sure you must have had nice people. Don't you want me to write to them?"

He was not interested, but he would do anything to please me. He finally gave a Boston address. Helena Dudley of the Boston Settlement, to whom the address was sent, found a decent family, an old father and a sister who was a milliner. A letter came from the sister: —

I can't help but be grateful to you for showing friendship to Peter. He has been nothing but a trouble to us all his life. We cannot both afford to make the journey, but if he wants to see his own people one of us will come.

I took this letter to Peter. He read it, then said briefly, "I 'd rather have the money."

I learned many lessons from Peter. One was a reconviction of the unlikelihood that a frail character in a frail body can march through life. Another was the unfailing chivalry that I have found among the weakest. I have never known it to fail. It must be deep in the minds of men even of the lowest spirit, that respect and therefore chivalry due women whom they believe to be good.

My first lesson in this was when I had been living on the East Side only a short time. A call came, and the message indicated a very sick child. I seized a bag and rushed out. The address was in Pearl Street. That street is not straight, and it is difficult to find numbers

on it.   Under one of the extension arches of Brooklyn
Bridge I saw three men.   It was dusk, they were roughly
dressed, and they looked a bit rowdy.   For a single moment I hesitated and was tempted to take the longer
route through Park Row, but I did not.   I kept to my
course and accosted the men.

"I am searching for this number on Pearl Street,"
I said, "and I don't know how to find it.   I have been
called to care for a sick child."

The men were at once all attention.

"Lady," said one of them, "this ain't a safe neighborhood for you and it's getting dark.   We'll go with
you."

And two of them did so, one carrying my bag, the
other tottering a little but not very much.   They took
me to the number.   The child was desperately in need
of care, and it was a long time before I finished.   When
I came down it was quite dark, but the two men were
waiting to escort me home.

Occasionally strangers who find their way to Henry
Street come because they want to observe a phase of
American life not always available to a visitor.   For
diplomatic reasons our hospitality has been asked from
Washington for foreign delegations.   Once we were
frankly told that a South American commission was under the impression that there is nothing to be seen in the
United States but the successful attainment of material ends.   The official to whom the delegation had been
entrusted felt that it was important for their understanding of this country that they should see something
of values other than those that are purchasable.   Of
course the hospitality of Henry Street was accorded.

A Near-by Market

One morning John D. Rockefeller, Jr., stopped for a brief discussion of a vice investigation under way by a special grand jury of which he was foreman. He was most earnest in his quest for clarifying fact and opinion. As he departed I opened the door to members of a German Chamber of Commerce delegation who had come to America to study similar groups and inquire into the moral influences said to be operating in American cities. When I told them who the visitor was that they had passed on the steps, and commented upon the sincerity of the many men and women of his generation who were studying the evils latent in our civilization and trying to remedy them, one of these Germans said: —

"The opposite is true in Germany. The strong and unselfish people of influence, best known in America as the Forty-Niners, have passed away. The people of the succeeding generation are bent on gain and entirely unresponsive to higher ideals."

Years ago my introduction to English men and women came through the Fabian Society. Honor Morton, friend of R. R. Bowker, had invited some members she considered interesting to meet her American guest, and from that introduction lifelong friendships have ensued. Graham Wallas, affectionately called "Wallas the Well-Beloved," was the first man resident we had. When he came to the United States he had letters to many distinguished people, but as he was then lecturing and had limited time it did not seem possible for him to present his introductions. I ventured to invite the people on the list for Sunday supper. Theodore Roosevelt, Jacob

Riis, Richard Watson Gilder, W. D. Howells, Felix Adler, Seth Low, Brander Matthews, are some of the names I recall.

After the party was over, our attractive guest was as interested as were we in discussing the significance of the coming of these busy people to a settlement on the lower East Side. It was before the days of the automobile, and to reach Henry Street was not simple. Yet everyone except Brander Matthews had come; it happened to be his birthday.

Theodore Roosevelt, then Police Commissioner, was escorted by Jacob Riis, his loyal friend. On the journey they had encountered an Italian who was "minding his pushcart" and was being nearly blown away by the gusts of that wintry night. "Teddy" was bubbling over with the fun of his interview with the peddler. T. R. had said to the man, "I don't see how you fellows make a living." The Italian shrugged and replied, "No good, no good. What I maka on de peanuta I lose on de dam' banan'." This was the first of many visits from T. R.

Later Ramsay MacDonald and his bride came to us because Fabian friends had told them they would see something of the "moral influence" that was leavening the Tammany lump of New York City politics. We were deep in preëlection organization, and the MacDonalds had opportunity to see us in action. The first night they arrived we took them to a mass meeting for which we were responsible in Apollo Hall, at that time a centre of local "machine" politics. Felix Adler, Dr. Rainsford, and other supposedly influential reformers (alas, we know better now than we did then what an election requires!) were to speak. But we were sold out. The pro-Tammany owner had rented another floor in the building for a "regular" meeting at the same hour of the same night. The audience there was accommodated with chairs, but there was not a single seat in the room we had secured at a high price. And many of the people who came to our gathering purposely scuffled and coughed and stumbled. Never was there a sadder failure! Next evening our party, with Professor Giddings and other sympathetic citizens, went to hear the election returns, and instructive it was to see the jubilant crowds and their banners of victory — "To Hell with Reform!"

The early visit to Henry Street of Ramsay MacDonald and his wife on their wedding trip was the beginning of a long association. And because "Chequers" and "10 Downing" and even "Hampstead" and "Lossiemouth" are known as inspiration points through the experience and the contributions to the world of the famous Prime Minister, my thoughts revert to the little home established in Lincoln's Inn Fields, where now stands a beautiful marble bench, placed there in memory of Margaret MacDonald by the Women's Labor League.

In 1927 came the Prime Minister for a brief holiday with the dear daughter, Ishbel. Mr. MacDonald's very serious illness during that visit made clear the affection in which he was held. I refrain from dwelling upon the tragedy of that interrupted trip, but cannot resist telling a story. The anxious doctors in the Philadelphia hospital felt that the institution's store of the brandy which was essential for him might be distasteful to the

Prime Minister, and they asked me whether I could secure a better grade. I telephoned Sir Joseph Duveen, the celebrated art collector and Mr. MacDonald's friend, who, being British and hospitable, might have maintained a cellar of pre-Prohibition stocks. The next morning brought Sir Joseph's secretary with historic bottles. One was selected for immediate use, and while the nurse was administering the dose I explained to the patient that it was 1815 French brandy, and that Sir Joseph Duveen had provided it. In feverish half-consciousness, the patient said: —

"Eighteen-fifteen — that's the time Tschaikowsky celebrated — that's about when Romney painted the beautiful Mrs. Davenport — " And he wandered on over the harmonies of that period.

In thanking Sir Joseph, I wrote him of what seemed to me an extraordinary revelation of the things that dwelt in the mind of this man. A telephone call from New York brought expressions of eager friendship from Sir Joseph: —

"I own 'Mrs. Davenport.' May I not bring the picture to the hospital and hang it in his room?"

The risk was too great for this almost priceless painting, and I thought it only right to refuse Sir Joseph. But the great authority on art answered: "I'd like to bring it over. There's nobody whose judgment on pictures I value so much as his."

When I was in England some months later I was asked why, when "Mrs. Davenport" went to the hospital to see the Prime Minister, she was not permitted to call!

When I read of Lord Lytton's illuminating report on

Manchuria it recalls a handsome visitor, for at Henry Street we remember Lord Lytton not so much for his broad understanding of international affairs as for his grace as a morris dancer. In the appropriate costume, with bells on his knees and flute at his lips, he made his own music as he danced round and round the gymnasium, to be followed by Chalif, whose athletic Russian dances were in striking contrast.

When Margaret Bondfield first came to visit us, she was not yet the Right Honorable Margaret Bondfield, Minister of Labor in the MacDonald Cabinet and only woman Privy Councilor of England; but when she spoke to an admiring audience in the Settlement it was plain to be seen that here was one who had developed a great philosophy out of her experience. Later she said in Montagu House, headquarters of the Labor Ministry, that her poverty and trials as a worker and a labor leader had all been a preparation for the office she held.

Sometimes we remember to ask our guests to record their visit in our Guest Book, and on the pages are the names of artists, actors, archæologists, leaders of forlorn causes, philanthropists, dancers, statesmen, scientists. Dr. Abraham Jacobi, whose broad interests as a physician form a unique chapter in American medical history, is on the same page with the militant suffragette, Mrs. Emmeline Pankhurst. There are mementos of the visit of the Japanese Red Cross Commission, a reminder of Ellen Terry's generous gift of her art to us, and Galsworthy's greetings.

Galsworthy and his wife came to New York when his play, *The Mob,* was attracting the attention of New

Yorkers to the Neighborhood Playhouse. Alice and
Irene Lewisohn were responsible for a notable production. People used all kinds of direct and indirect influence to get seats. Galsworthy, whose presence in
New York was not known, telephoned to the little
theatre.

"No tickets," said the girl at the box office. "Who's
talking?"

"John Galsworthy. My wife and I should like very
much to see the play."

The girl was not to be hoodwinked. Said she, as she
slammed down the telephone, "Quit your kiddin'!"

No one is more welcome to the House than Helen
Keller, whom we love. And she has a genius for finding words for great truths. Her comment on our busy
programme was: "Sympathy without works is like eyes
without light."

Mary Macarthur, revered figure among labor women
in England, accompanied the delegates to that first international labor conference in Washington. Her name
in our Guest Book recalls to me a painful incident that
I hesitate to write, but it did happen and it might as
well be told. The treaty makers at Versailles had con-
ceded Woodrow Wilson's point that the Labor Covenant
should be included in the treaty itself, and had incor-
porated it in Article XIII. President Wilson had immediately issued the invitation for the first meeting under this article to convene in Washington.

But alas, when the delegates reached Washington
much water had flowed under the bridge — the treaty
had been repudiated, President Wilson had been stricken,

the election had brought another party into power. Nobody felt the responsibility, hardly even the impulse of hospitality, for the delegates who had arrived at the President's invitation. They found nobody to welcome them and no arrangements had been made. The meeting place, the Pan-American Building, had been secured by the forethought of the English international acting secretary, who had also purchased note pads and pencils. Women's organizations did assume the obligation of occasional entertainment. Somewhat sardonically, the only official gesture was a trip to Mount Vernon aboard a Navy craft, and this was urged upon our Secretary of the Navy by his wife, whose Southern instincts of hospitality were doubtless outraged by the neglect of these guests. The European delegates, who met as strangers, made entertainment for themselves and cemented friendships that have endured through the years. There was some slight balm in the supper given for the international labor delegates at Henry Street, when they were encouraged to "explode" their disappointment and to realize that, though Washington had failed, many Americans were deeply concerned with their mission and disturbed by the fiasco of the conference reception.

Another visitor whose concern was first of all with labor was Keir Hardie. We were both busy and had no chance for what he called "thorough talk," so we agreed to breakfast together. He was grieved to find in this country so little sense of sacrifice on the part of the wage earners. At the time, there was a strike in Troy and he went there to see the picket line and to study the situation. He commented on the attractive

girls in their crisp, fresh dresses, but he was quite shocked
when he learned that they did not do their own laundry
work and that they even had their nails manicured! He
did not question their right to these small luxuries, but
he was disturbed that they were willing to spend money
on nonessentials when "the cause" needed funds. He
was even more shocked when he found that a threatened
strike at the Eastman Kodak plant in Rochester was organized in protest against the inadequate parking space
provided for employees' cars. His was the bewilderment of the stranger over the American standard of
living in "normal" times. How splendid was the spirit
of the man is revealed in the page he inscribed in our
Guest Book: —

Underlying Socialism is the great basic truth of human
equality; not that all are to be alike, but that all are to be
equal, which is a very different thing. Under Socialism
there would be no exploiting class, no tyranny of one sex
or race over another. Socialism would give reality to the
claim so often insisted upon from the Christian pulpit, and
yet so universally belied by our everyday deeds, that God
hath made of one blood all the nations of the earth to dwell
together in unity.

Doubtless the physical fact of sitting on a dais and
listening to petitioners from a lower level establishes a
barrier that impedes the message before it reaches its
receiving station. One is entirely justified in recognizing the psychological implications. I remember that
the members of the Board of Estimate and Apportion-
ment, the body that controls our municipal purse strings

in New York City, sitting at our simple supper table, listened without inhibitions to the needs of school children for improved methods of physical supervision. And the children were uppermost in their minds when they officially — on the dais — voted the essential appropriation. Business men have employed opportunities for getting together as human beings to accomplish a "deal," and loyalties for altruistic ends admit similar stimulus.

The "Man from Dahomey," a picturesque stranger, I met when an institution for the homeless in our neighborhood invited Mary Antin and me to a Passover service. It was the custom of this centre to gather in for the sacred festival the homeless and the immigrants detained at Ellis Island. The host of the evening, gowned in his shroud,[1] reclined on a couch according to the ritual, and the guests, most of them men who were strangers from distant lands, were all familiar with the ceremony. In a far corner of the room I noticed a black man, and when I commented on his presence at this Hebrew festival one of the staff told me he was a Jew. The man was called over, a tall, erect figure with dark skin, straight hair, and a nose slightly aquiline. My equilibrium was nearly lost when he addressed me in English with a Scotch burr.

He was from Dahomey, on the Slave Coast of Africa.

---

[1] On this point an informed friend writes: "One of the most beautiful things in the Jewish religion is the thought that before God in death every Jew has the same status, and it is therefore an old custom among the Orthodox, on their holidays, to wear the white garment, called the shroud, in which they are to be buried when their time comes."

He explained that his tribe had always been distinctive in Dahomey because they proclaimed their belief in one god and one wife, and because they had never been cannibals. Many of their neighbors, he stated, adhered to the barbaric custom. "Indeed," he added with some pride, "when religious fervor moves Dahomey people to cannibalism they often come down to our tribe, who are weavers and industrious workers, and eat them." ("Quite a compliment, in a way," one of our party murmured.) The man from Dahomey had, as a stowaway, reached Scotland, where a philanthropic gentleman took him under his wing and had him educated. He had always planned to return to Africa and give his people the benefit of his education. The French had identified the tribe as Hebrews because of their customs, and brought to them the Bible which had been translated for the Abyssinians. This stranger was then under study by Franz Boas, the famous anthropologist at Columbia University, and, to make sure the Jew from Dahomey with his Scotch burr was not spoofing me, I turned to Professor Boas, who corroborated the fact of this remarkable Slave Coast tribe.

From the Arctic regions came a man who showed in the errand which brought him that geographical boundaries never really divide, and that people who care for humanity arrive at identical realizations. Through Henry Goddard Leach, that devoted interpreter of Scandinavia, we came to know Hjalmar Lundbohn, called the "King of Lapland." This man, a geologist, who attained a position of authority in Swedish industry, had taken 30,000 Swedes to work in the iron mines in Lapland. He was eager to provide every modern cultural advantage for these transplanted workers, that their migration should not be a loss to them. He was interested in the Lapps, also, a nomadic people whom he refused to employ underground because he was sure such work would destroy them. The particular errand that brought him to Henry Street was the problem of the six-hour working day, for which the Swedes had asked. This understanding man said, "Six hours is a long day to toil beneath the earth. I would willingly accede to the request except for the fact that the people have had no training in using leisure, and eighteen hours of unemployment might be disastrous. I want to find out what you people do to help your friends use their unemployed time in creative, helpful pleasure and instruction."

Weddings that have been celebrated at the House have ranged from those of residents and their chosen mates to the Armenian wedding for which we had to search New York and its environs to find a bishop who could perform the ceremony. It seemed inauspicious to have the newly arrived and lovely bride make her vows in a language she did not know. When we did find the bishop (in Hoboken), he put on a most gorgeous robe and patiently taught us a complicated ceremonial.

Trouble as well as pleasure has brought visitors. A district attorney once insisted that more crimes had been confessed voluntarily to me than to him. There seems to be a widely felt need for a confessional. Certainly I cannot flatter myself that the people who have gone out of their way to confide in me came for advice.

I doubt whether anyone ever followed advice I gave. What they really wanted was to tell their trouble — sometimes their crime — to someone who would forget.

A lovely young woman, a leader in her circle, one day stopped me on the stairs. I cannot forget her desperate eyes, the flutter of her breath and of her hands as she told me that she must see me alone. Closeted in my room, she said: "I want to tell you something. There was a man I loved. He could n't marry me. Perhaps I would n't have married him. But I stayed with him. And I never told my mother. It 's the only thing I ever kept from her. It gnaws at me. Must I tell her?"

What she had done haunted her. But I entreated her not to tell her mother, pointing out that it was of the past, and she would only make her mother suffer to no purpose. And I asked her when she saw me to forget that she had told me this. She had kept her secret for a long time and she was worn with the weight of it. The fact that I shared it might have spoiled our friendship, but it did not. And, having passed on her "sin," it no longer tormented her. She went her gentle way in peace once more.

Perhaps this chapter should be closed by quoting one of our simplest neighbors, who, in trying to formulate her evaluation of the Settlement, said to another neighbor, "I 'll tell you what — what you get out of this house you can't take away in your pocket."

IV

NURSING AND HEALTH

DOUBTLESS among the outstanding phenomena within the memory of the living are the vast sums and the vast educational programmes that have been poured out in efforts to care for the sick, to prevent illness, and to popularize the subject of health.

Perhaps no work that is at once scientific and immediately concerned with the happiness and well-being of men and women ever bestowed benefits comparable to those achieved in the struggle toward a higher level of health. The results are rewarding. There is evidence of an informed and widespread interest in health as essential to the good life, though there are great fields still to be covered and countless people still to be reached. The fact that many devastating diseases have been controlled — and some almost eliminated — through the intelligent application of new knowledge and techniques has proved the validity of modern science. Tuberculosis is waning, infants who survive the first month of their existence have far greater expectation of life, and, to quote Dr. Louis I. Dublin: "We Americans can look forward to living twice as long as did our forefathers a century and a half ago, when the average span of life was only thirty-five years." For example, in New York City, diphtheria approaches extinction through the outstanding efforts of the present Commissioner of Health, Dr. Shirley T. Wynne. In industry, "phossy jaw" is no longer the terror of the match workers. We have recognized the hazards of lead poisoning, silicosis, fatigue poison, and many other perils; and industrial education and protective legislation have worked to guard against them. These examples are cited simply as demonstrating accomplishments that encourage physician, nurse, and philanthropist to believe that the day may soon dawn when we Americans can enjoy a measure of life and health that is consistent with our extraordinary resources and the intelligence of our people.

The torch lighting the path is the certainty that illness is to a great extent preventable. Each achievement seems to prophesy another. One cannot touch upon this subject without tribute to the Rockefeller Foundation, which has shown statesmanship of the highest order, — as have the Rosenwald, Milbank, and other great Funds, — and without also mentioning the effective work of the League of Nations Medical Service.

Experts have interpreted for scientists and for the

laity the trends of medical erudition. The Metropolitan
Life Insurance Company, through Dr. Louis I. Dublin,
its distinguished statistician, has done notable service
in this field. Advertising campaigns, the movies, the
radio: practically every device has been intelligently
exploited, that we might some day achieve "Erewhon,"
so alluringly described in Samuel Butler's famous book
— the title of which really is, alas, "Nowhere." The
subject is vast, and is interwoven with so many aspects
of life that it would be impossible for any writer to
attempt more than a rapid review within the confines of
a single chapter.

I hope I shall not be charged with lacking a sense
of proportion if I stress the purpose, the growth, and
the importance of the public health nurse in the general
progress of the public health. I feel that I am justified
in this because her place in the development of the care
and education of the sick is so seldom recorded — though
among those who know her in action her value is duly
appreciated. President Hoover's Research Committee
on Social Trends reported that public health nurses,
who in 1909 counted only 1413, in 1931 numbered
15,865; and added, "The importance of the public
health nurse cannot well be overestimated." Yet it is
only forty years since the writer, with her friend, began this work in the homes of New York City, and
defined the service as "Public Health Nursing."

Those familiar with the nurses are amazingly impressed by the quality of their work and the initiative
they take, not only in their profession but in the social
problems so intimately identified with their service.

They are the indispensable carriers of the findings of the scientists and the laboratories to the people themselves, using their sympathy and training to make as intelligible as language permits the facts of health and life. What a change is this from the priestly secrecy of the old-fashioned medical practitioner! Educators, whether in this field or another, realize that different methods must be employed to meet different degrees of intelligence; and that the receptivity can best be gauged by the instructor. It is evident that the success of the nurse flows from her unparalleled opportunity for explaining, and for making a teaching demonstration of every treatment she gives. The sickroom becomes the classroom, and the value of her lesson does not diminish because it must needs be given in the simplest form.

The famous Dr. William H. Welch, of Johns Hopkins University, declared that America has made three original contributions to public health: the sanitation of the Canal Zone, the State Tuberculosis Laboratories instituted by Dr. Hermann Biggs, and the public health nurse.

When Reni-Mal, the official French painter whose posters familiarized a war-ridden world with the plight of the *poilu,* sought after the War to find an American type to stand as a personification of what he held to be this country's gift, he decided upon the public health nurse as the "Unique American." The dignity and beauty of the Henry Street staff member who became his model are signalized by the honored place the picture holds in the Central Administration Building. It has been widely reproduced as the symbol of nursing service, as well as the broad spirit of altruism of our country.

The profession of nursing has an honorable background. The old and the new are linked together: except for the period held up to ridicule by Dickens, the same traits have been shown from the abbess ancestors to Florence Nightingale and on to the American development — the spirit of consecration, the power of organization, the realization that the nurse is an effective and indispensable educator, and that her profession is of community importance. Each advance has been but a new graft on an age-old acceptance of her duties and devotion.

Some years ago I addressed a graduating class in a hospital in Kyoto, Japan. A modern doctor had taken the initiative there in establishing a training school. I faced the kimono-clad students who sat on the floor, hoping through my address to trace with them the part women have played in this profession from the earliest manifestations of womanly tenderness and skill. I began by saying that I did not know the legends of Japan, but I was certain that no country could achieve a great civilization which did not cherish traditions of women who had given all they had to help the race. Before the interpreter could begin, the presiding physician stopped him and excitedly exclaimed in his halting English: "Madam, you see that Buddha in the corner?" — directing my attention to a beautiful bronze. "That Buddha," said he, "was brought from a temple dedicated to the Empress who four thousand years ago sat by the roadside and washed the feet of the lepers!"

Throughout the ages the same roots produced medicine and nursing, but different forces or motives influenced the two groups. Medicine's advance has accompanied the desire and the opportunity for scientific research, while nursing seems to have been more closely tied to waves of religious awakening, of social and humanitarian effort. Medicine declined in the early centuries of the Christian era. Organized nursing began as a branch of religious service, and in the early Middle Ages occupied a position of great authority in the care of the sick. It was, indeed, of a higher intellectual and social status than the secular profession of medicine at that time. Later medicine gained control, almost complete control, of the nursing orders and organizations, and this period does not reflect credit on either branch of the healing art. Recognition was accorded more in polite than in serious terms. Nursing became the "handmaid of the physician," the "official wife of medicine," and was sometimes referred to as the "younger sister" of the medical family. Nurses now assert the essential independence of their profession, and in this they are supported by the intelligent medical leaders, who agree that the fields are fairly distinct — that the nurse is the logical associate of the doctor, and that there is interchange of duties. Of late years the practitioners have handed over to the nurses some of the offices which were at one time the exclusive responsibility of the doctors. The physicians recognize the nurse's share in modern medical science, and the relationship is enhanced in dignity and value by the attitude of the groups toward one another.

The struggle to obtain the more dignified position was difficult because there was for a long time an acceptance of submission to absolute hospital management and to commercial middlemen, and the nurses had no voice in their own affairs. There was stubborn resistance to the emergence of the nurse from these controls, which seemed to cling like barnacles. Mrs. Bedford Fenwick, of England, an intrepid leader, organized the opposition; she finally secured government recognition of nursing as a profession, with state examination and the right of nurses to sit on the examining board or council. The nurse question had become the woman question. A Royal Charter, granted in 1887, was the first one ever given to a body of professional women in England. In America and other new countries, the nurse's independence was achieved with relatively slight struggle. The international group soon crystallized; it now maintains headquarters in Geneva, and its members are definitely helpful to each other.

The history of nursing is fascinating reading, and nurses are indebted to three beloved leaders for the distinguished presentation of their saga: M. Adelaide Nutting, Lavinia L. Dock, and Isabel M. Stewart.[1] The writer and her friend, who were responsible for the establishment of the Henry Street Service, declared

[1] *History of Nursing,* by M. Adelaide Nutting and Lavinia L. Dock, revised 1921; iv vols. *A Short History of Nursing,* by Lavinia L. Dock and Isabel M. Stewart; revised 1931.

themselves committed to a twin service of ministration and education, and from the beginning there was encouraging demonstration that this dedication promised timely rescue from ignorance and neglect.

Upon the walls of the study in the Nurses' Building a map of the world is stretched. The pins that pierce the map indicate every country in which a Henry Street nurse has either initiated or assisted in the public health nursing service. With a single exception, every country has a pin stuck in it. To meet the earnest messengers of help to far-off peoples is a never-failing gratification.

Two attractive young women, dressed in our uniforms, rose from a Negro congregation I was addressing one night. They wanted to identify themselves, lest I might not know that they were training with us. They told with pride how they were sent from Liberia and were to return there better equipped to help their own people. The many Philippine nurses who have been with us remain loyal to our principles and write of the "Henry Street spirit" which permeates their organization. A continuing fellowship is maintained with those who work as public health nurses in China and Japan, the Scandinavian countries, Palestine, Russia, Siberia, Mexico, and other lands, and give eloquent evidence of the tie that binds.

The increasing importance of the nursing profession is shown not only by its growth but by its broadening interests. Current press references to the 1933 International Conference of Nurses in Paris include as a matter of course discussions of social insurance, old-age pensions, state aid, and so forth. The programme indicates an intelligent comprehension of professional obligations and authority. This is not, I hasten to say, at the cost of the nurse's traditional function. Indeed, the nursing care in which Henry Street has had most experience and most interest serves as a continuing reminder that the attributes of the nurse of to-day are strengthened, enriched, and reënforced by her amplified training and enlarged responsibilities.

A student of progress in human relations is no longer confused about the profession as was a bank teller whom I recall with amusement. I was carrying to the savings bank the books of our Settlement boys and girls and their elders, and the courtesy of immediate attention was, as usual, accorded me. Said the official at the desk: "Could you please explain your interest in savings? I thought nurses were healers." So sensitive was my mind to political aspersions that I thought he meant "heelers," and rushed to the defense of our conduct.

The nurse of to-day is an outgrowth of many influences. Isabel Hampton Robb first proclaimed the need for better preparation for nurses in executive and teaching positions, and she and her associates found at Teachers College, Columbia University, a readiness to inaugurate suitable courses. M. Adelaide Nutting was given a full professorship. When the demands for public health nurses became pressing, Henry Street supported the expansion of the courses by helping to secure the needed money. This innovation in university instruction, which began with two pupils in 1899, has increased to seven hundred and fifty-two in 1933, with three hundred and thirty summer students — a total of over one thousand students, many of whom carry on part-time study while engaged in their professional duties.

Because of the spectacular growth of public health nursing, universities have provided educational facilities to meet the need; and in New York, at least, theory and practice are united by using Henry Street for field-work, giving the students the advantage of its matchless clinical material. This field training also has been made available, as far as expedient, to the undergraduates in the nursing schools, the students themselves demanding that this be included in their training. The privilege of such fieldwork is granted with careful selection of students, their number limited to those that can be assimilated and suitably educated.

Invaluable progress was afforded by the study of nursing made through the Rockefeller generosity, under a committee whose chairman was Professor C.-E. A. Winslow of Yale, whose never-failing enthusiasm for the nurses' accomplishment is a very real stimulus.[2] Josephine Goldmark ably directed the study. Membership on the committee was composed of deans of medical colleges and universities and prominent educators among the nurses — assuring a careful, unbiased presentation. That study showed that there existed lamentable deficiencies in many of the training schools: primitive teaching methods, and often what amounted to exploitation of promising young women. Though the com-

[2] *Nursing and Nursing Education in the United States*, Committee to Study Visiting Nursing, 1922.

mittee represented many points of view, the Henry Street Settlement records with pleasure that the committee, under its roof, unanimously accepted the recommendations. The immediate result of the study was the inauguration of the School of Nursing at Yale University. Annie Goodrich, then director of the Henry Street Settlement Nursing Service and professor in the Teachers College department, was chosen to be dean of the school. This marks an era in the history of nursing. While Yale was not the first university to grant nursing degrees, it was the first to demand college preparation for admission — at the start, two years; now full college training. It is also fortunate in the possession of a separate endowment (a Rockefeller gift) and its own dean — not the dean of the medical school.

Later a study,[3] made by the Committee on the Grading of Nursing Schools, resulted in the wiping out of many training schools unable to give the essential diversity of training to their students; and a second valuable result has been the engagement by hospitals of graduate staffs. These methods help meet to some extent the problem of overproduction in the nursing profession, particularly in the private-duty field.

Henry Street has always insisted both that there was an unnecessary expenditure of money for the full-time nurse and that the nurse's time was frequently wasted by the too ready call for her exclusive service. It has offered as a dual economy its particular type of service, for patients who are sick at home. The importance of this plan is emphasized by the knowledge first that

[3] *Nurses, Patients, and Pocketbooks*, by May A. Burgess, 1928.

90 per cent of the persons who are ill are ill in their homes, and secondly that hospitals stagger under heavy deficits; consequently there should be intelligent sifting of the patients sent to the hospitals.

The recent lean years have been reflected in Henry Street's records by an excessive increase in the number of patients and a decrease in even the nominal sums paid by them; also by decreased contributions from the public; and finally by an increase in the calls upon us by people who in other days would almost certainly have employed the full-time private-duty nurse.

The nurses sent from Henry Street and similar nursing organizations are very carefully selected for personality, adaptability, and aptitude; their educational background is carefully investigated; they are given careful technical training before admission to the field, and are continuously supervised by the more experienced members of the staff assigned to this duty. I dwell upon the perfected organization because it is not always understood that this service is comparable to the hospital service, where patients who can pay, who can pay little, or who can pay nothing at all receive the care suited to their needs.

The comparative cost to the community of hospital as contrasted to home care is great enough to warrant a subsidy to the nursing service from municipalities similar to that which has been long and properly accorded to the hospitals for the indigent. The prejudice toward such subsidy in some communities must be overcome. A good illustration is the relative cost to the community of hospitalization and home care for contagious disease. These diseases are generally seasonal, but the expensive investment in hospital plant and overhead continues throughout the year. The need for a contagious hospital in the Borough of the Bronx has been agitated for some time, and a study was made by the State Charities Aid in 1932. Marguerite Wales, director of the Henry Street Visiting Nurse Service, was responsible for the inclusion in this study of some interesting data as to the facilities available for home care in the Bronx. The investigation revealed that more patients ill from the four common communicable diseases were cared for by our visiting nurses than by hospitals. The report states that "the low mortality among the patients under private medical care using the nursing service bears eloquent testimony to the favorable results of a high-grade quality of visiting nursing in the care of contagion. The ratio of deaths to cases is extremely low." [4]

An important recommendation was made by the committee sponsoring this study: "That formal provision be made by the City for the bedside nursing care of suitable cases of acute communicable disease in their homes, through competent, organized nursing services."

In the light of this report, we look back upon the early days of Henry Street when the provision for the care of people sick from communicable diseases was borne in upon us as an essential part of our work. The incidence of cross-infections, so difficult to prevent in

[4] *Survey of Communicable Disease Hospital Needs, Borough of Bronx*, Phillips, 1932, p. 48.

hospitals, induced Dr. Lederle, an outstanding Health Commissioner of New York City, to permit our staff to care for the reported cases which remained at home. The disinfecting stations of the Department of Health were made available to the nurses, and calls to contagious cases were answered only after other cases were cared for. The demonstration gave convincing proof that patients could be cared for at home, at comparatively small cost, and at no danger of carrying the disease. In fact, in all the forty years of Henry Street's experience with such patients, there has not been one instance recorded of a nurse carrying infection. It is a matter of deep regret that this early successful demonstration was discontinued with political changes in the city.

Henry Street itself, through its generalized service, continued to care for communicable-disease cases, the technique being approved by the Commissioner of Health and the Advisory Medical Committee. In a five-year study made by Miss Wales from our records, it was found that in scarlet fever alone our service had tripled from 1928 to 1932, with a very favorable mortality rate. Our entire communicable-disease programme for that year covered more than 10 per cent of these diseases reported in the Boroughs we serve.

Dr. Charles Hendee Smith, well-known pediatrician, states that the home is the best place for a sick child. He makes, of course, exceptions when surgical care or special therapy is necessary, when obscure diseases are to be treated, or when hopeless home conditions are found; but he declares that in general the great majority of childhood diseases can best be cared for at home, and that the aid of a visiting nurse gives the supervision that is essential.

Throughout this book I have related stories culled from the nurses' reports which show how venturesome and often romantic are their rounds, and how the encouragement that comes from the devotion and appreciation of the patient plays a large part in the nurse's continuing enthusiasm. She is heartened not only by this response to her ministrations but also by the realizable results of the teaching she has given. Two notes from patients speak for themselves.

My dear Miss M——:

I hope you are well. . . . We are all feeling good here T.G.[5] Only my husband, he has been off work since you were up here with a very bad cold like the Flu. . . . I took care of him and done what I could. . . . I kept him away from everyone of the kiddies and I boiled everything he used and washed myself in Lysol and kept an apron I put on when I went in to him so you see I am trying to be careful as I can, all from your good training.

The second note indicates the concern of the father as well as of the mother: —

Please I would like, if you were very kind enough, to do all what you could with my kid. My wife does n't speak very fluent but she could understand some English, but to make it ease for you, I 'm going to explain what 's wrong with my son. He is suffering from the adenoids and tonsils and during the day and by nights he inhales and exhales by the mouth and he does n't give any use at all to his nose for

[5] "Thank God."

respiration.   My idea is to know what should I have to do in order to have him operated on.   Both things.   Thanks.

This individual need but illustrates the larger requirements and the open spaces that invite attention. We learned with shocking vividness during the War how many of the handicaps from which our youths suffered could have been corrected in childhood.   The knowledge gave new impetus to tend the neglected field, and a heavy responsibility has been placed upon the shoulders of the nurse, so well equipped to give education.   Increasing emphasis is laid on detecting and overcoming defects in children — cardiac, dental, visual, aural, and others.   In this effort it may be repeated that the nurse is the indispensable interpreter of the aims and methods of modern medical science.   Indeed, the nurse who does her work well helps the doctor immeasurably — particularly the young doctor.   Perhaps, too, his social enthusiasm is kindled by witnessing the almost immediate effect of the care in the home as well as on the patients.

One physician tells with exceeding appreciation of a patient he had reported in the morning.   When he returned in the afternoon and opened the door of the home, he was positive he had made a mistake, because the room looked unfamiliar.   When he had verified the address and reëntered, he found that the transformation had been effected by the nurse's visit.   She had changed a dark, stuffy sickroom to a bright and airy one.   The shutters had been opened, the dingy window washed; crisp white curtains had been put up, the grimy floors were scrubbed; the meagre furniture was dusted and neatly arranged; the patient bathed and her hair combed, and the bed made up with fresh linen. A white-covered table with the necessary sickroom supplies was ready for the doctor at the patient's bedside. The nurse had summoned the husband from his job, with the consent of his boss, and he had toiled as hard as she in accomplishing this miracle.

Maternity cases offer great and surprising opportunity, not only for the care given to the patient but for rearranging what might seem to be a hopeless scene. Touching are the evidences of the value put upon this service by the people themselves. We have not yet been able to secure at Henry Street money to give a twenty-four-hour service throughout the city, but in one extended area our nurses respond to calls for maternity care day or night. In addressing a group of impoverished women from whom I wished to learn their evaluation of the different services available to them, I asked which of all the forms of relief were most prized. With one voice they said, "The nurse who comes when the baby comes."

For it was likely, when a child was to be born, that the women in the neighborhood would crowd around the mother's bed, offering their advice and their untrained assistance. When the ambulance doctor arrived for the delivery, he was often brusque. Sometimes he forgot to remove his hat.

Difficult to describe the difference the nurse makes! Before the confinement, she has made the acquaintance of the mother, and the supplies needed are in the home.

When the woman's time comes, the nurse makes the bed according to the best hospital procedure, and sends the neighbors and the children away; and when the doctor arrives it is to a place prepared with the seemliness and dignity that make the birth of the child the event of solemn importance that it should be.

This is the kind of note that comes to the nurse's desk: "My mother has told me that you took care of her and me when I was born and I would like to come to see you. Is that all right?" There is a sad reflection in this, for the long ties of sentiment, I fear, are an indication of the few friendly encounters that the family must have had in the first struggling days of adjustment to this country.

Nor is this vital ministration available only to women in the congested districts of great cities. Far from any metropolis, a valiant band of nurses works heroically for the wives and babies of mountaineers. The story of the nurses' adventurous lives, often traveling miles on horseback over narrow, lonely trails to reach the scattered homes of their patients, is an epic of pioneer courage and resourcefulness.[6] It is pleasant to record that Henry Street has some share in this achievement through occasional interchange of staff members.

The nurses in the home caring for the chronic sick often solve pathetic problems. A recent study of chronic sickness discloses how little is known of it by the general public, perhaps because it is less dramatic as well as less frequent than brief, acute illness. This study of *Chronic Illness in New York City,* under the

[6] *Nurses on Horseback,* by Ernest Poole, 1932.

auspices of the Welfare Council, has shown that, with the exception of information upon tuberculosis, cancer, and mental disease, there is little available data. Even to those more or less familiar with New York conditions, it is surprising to learn that there are more children than old people among chronic invalids. While chronic disease is generally associated with old age, nevertheless birth injuries, accidents, and the after-effects of epidemics of childhood diseases have taken a heavy toll of the youngsters, and the majority of New York's chronic invalids are not old, but young. This study shows the cost of institutional care, to the family and to the community, and points out: —

Many chronic patients requiring skilled nursing can be suitably cared for at home, provided that regular visits from a nurse can be assured; otherwise, expensive hospital care must be provided, possibly over a long period.

But to give this requires larger support, since care for these patients must give way to the pressing demands made when acute diseases multiply or when epidemics break out. The chronic sick present many trying problems. The poor victims are often difficult and exhaust the sympathy of their families, though there are, of course, pleasing exceptions to this. In the homes with a small income the situation requires many aids.

In answer to a call, a Henry Street nurse found a woman partly paralyzed on her poor bed in a house on Madison Street. Her husband was a street cleaner. Before he left in the early morning he lifted his wife

MOTHERHOOD

into a chair and pushed it near the stove, that she might prepare the food for the children. She remained in that chair all the wearisome day until the return of her husband. The nurse realized the importance of this mother to the family, but also its cost to her in pain and fatigue. We begged the Street Cleaning Commissioner to change the man's station to the blocks near the tenement home, and also to grant the privilege of the man's help at home for fifteen minutes a day, the nurse pledging his return to the broom within that period. The Commissioner approved, the arrangement was made, and the plan worked like a charm. At ten-thirty in the morning the nurse appeared, gave the patient her bath, made the bed, completed her toilet. She then went down the stairs and beckoned the sweeper. He lifted the woman to her chair and without delay returned to his work for the city. The household, now well organized, kept mother, father, and four children knit together in a family unit. After the day's work the sweeper returned to the home and lifted the wife back to bed; with her shortened day and better care, she was not too exhausted to give housewifely supervision to dinner preparations and the other home duties shared by husband and children. Through the nurse, the children found broadened interests and recreation in the Settlement clubs and classes.

V

NURSING AND HEALTH (*Continued*)

HENRY STREET has long proclaimed the waste of visiting
nurses employed by many organizations rather than
maintained by one group. Years ago, when we were
trying to make our point, we told not only of the
wasted money and wasted time, but also of the loss in
effectiveness where, in those days, five or six different
nurses might be sent in by agencies, each interested only
in one phase of health, sickness, or propaganda. It was
possible to find a single home the confused focus of
attention from tuberculosis nurses sent by the city, by
the fraternal organization, by the church, and by relief
agencies. Those days have gone; but there are still the
unconverted who do not realize that the public health
nurse is the family health worker, and that the success
of her mission is to a great extent dependent upon the

elimination of conflicting responsibility and of all red tape.

The proof of this was well shown in a district supervised by one of our nurses. In a very small area, nine cases of typhoid came to her for care, each having been reported by a different group. One was referred by a janitress; the police referred one; family and doctors referred the others. The same nurse answered all the calls. Intelligent, immediate action on her part disclosed the common source of the disease — not milk or water, but a supply of raw fruit. There may have been nine different doctors; but there was only one nurse, and this made possible the prompt comprehension of the situation. Henry Street has long urged the value of a generalized service with specialized supervision, rather than a specialized nursing service. It is gratifying to know that public health demonstrations have supported this point of view, and that the emphasis has shifted from specialized to general service and to the wider recognition of the visiting nurse as the family health agent.

Adventures accompany the nurse on her rounds of homes faced with sudden emergency or burdened with chronic illness. The stories the nurses bring back from the day's work are often as gay as they are sad, and show how she exercises ingenuity and imagination in the fulfillment of her purpose.

From our Jamaica, Long Island, office comes a tale of the difficulties in transportation. There was a call for a nurse with the vague directions that when she reached the highway the policeman in the traffic booth would point out the road. But when the nurse reached the place the usual traffic officer was not there, a man who knew nothing about the family she was to visit was on duty, and an unusually high tide was running, making identification of the address very difficult.

"I found a man willing to try to guide me," said the nurse, "but wading through the swamp in that thick fog made a hard trip."

At the house she found the doctor, who had had equal difficulties, and bad luck in his effort to overcome them — for he had slipped and fallen as he splashed through the tide marsh. No preparations for the expected birth had been made. There was not even running water in the house, and, as salt water could not be used for sterilizing instruments, the father was sent in a rowboat to a neighbor's pump. On the same trip he went to the drug store for essential supplies. On her return visits for the next few days, the nurse found that the tides were rising higher. It was necessary to cross the marsh in a boat. Her oarsman was an eight-year-old child of a neighbor, who waited for her daily. Except for the transportation problem, the mother, the baby, and the family made it a "good case."

Out of a routine call during this lean year comes also the cherished story of "Mr. Noah." "Mr. Noah," as he was soon nicknamed, owns a boat, which he bought for ten dollars, and thereby was able to strike from his budget a costly item, "Rent." But Mr. Noah had a strong feeling for home; and he and his wife have made one out of that old boat. The site of his estate is on Park Avenue up in the 130's, where the Harlem

River divides Harlem and the Bronx. The place is an object of real interest to the suburbanites who see it daily from the train windows as they travel to and from town. Overhead is the trestle of the railroad, and its supporting pillars form natural compartments. Within that shelter one hundred and fifty men lived during the past winter. Here they ate, slept, washed their clothing, and organized and ran their own local government, emphasizing rules of sanitation and neatness — all under the dynamic leadership of Mr. Noah. The odd jobs they were able to secure provided essentials of food, soap, and tobacco for the group. Their shelter they provided themselves, using old packing cases, odd bits of lumber, pieces of linoleum, building paper, and corrugated iron. The whole company managed to keep off the bread lines. The atmosphere of their community was orderly and tranquil. The soft dirt rose over the nurse's shoes as she took her way to Mr. Noah's boat, from which her call had come. The bow of the boat rested on shore, and the gentle slope took the stern into deep water. Approach to this home disclosed a well and a garden, the garden enclosed by a wall built of wooden boxes. A little gate was latched across the path to the door. In the garden were growing cucumbers, squash, tomatoes, pole beans, two umbrella trees, and an old Christmas tree. The sign, "Beware the Dog," is important, as there are six dogs, ranging from the police-mixed-with-bull to a pup in which Irish terrier predominates.

A new baby was expected in Mr. Noah's family. Justifiable pride on the part of the owner required that the nurse go over the house boat — five quite comfortable rooms arranged triplex fashion, with two bedrooms and a shower bath downstairs, living room and kitchen on the middle floor, and the "music room" on top. The "music room" is equipped with a home-made radio and an upright piano purchased for two dollars. The home is lighted with electricity generated by a dynamo built and installed by Mr. Noah. The courtesy and appreciation of this family are heartening to the nurse. It is worth noting that the house boat is within the area in which the patients receive night service at the time of confinement, and the nurse who answered the night call found her way without mishap to the river.

To give another picture of our service, reference at least should be made to Henry Street's coöperation with the various demonstrations that are made from time to time. The Maternity Centre Association was organized in 1917 by a group which included the General Director of the Henry Street service. It was felt that greater attention would be focused on maternity work if it was developed as a special service. A restricted area was selected and demonstration made of the results of intensive nursing care to patients from the prenatal period through confinement and up to the time the physician returned for final post-partum examination.

Another small group whose contribution to the field of public health is important is the East Harlem Nursing and Health Service, with its public health programme. Four agencies, including our own Henry Street service, coöperate in this scheme to demonstrate what can be done with adequate funds and an adequate staff, carrying on a generalized service in a limited district. Henry Street reckons this as one of its centres, and contributes to it money in proportion to the size and population, and, as well, the fees contributed by patients, who pay according to their means, as in our other nursing centres of the city. The generous foundations aid in carrying on this adventure in resources pooled for the best results. This service is of particular value as a teaching centre, and is used by many nurses both native and from abroad.

The Bellevue-Yorkville Health Demonstration, which has been carried on since 1925 in a limited area on the East Side, through the generous support of the Milbank Memorial Fund, has afforded the city an excellent opportunity to demonstrate the value of various special services. Henry Street operates one of its centres here, and has coöperated in every way with the Health Department programme.

In 1929 the Commissioner of Health began his programme of district health centres. Harlem Health Centre is the first of these groups, and is an excellent example of coöperation between the public and private agencies. With the Commissioner, we look forward to the day when similar health centres can be established throughout the city.

In any story of nursing I cannot ignore the superb community rally at the time of the devastating influenza epidemic in 1918, with nurses playing their part in leadership and in the ranks. Perhaps this could have occurred only once, and only in New York City. The

Red Cross summoned relief organizations and social workers late one afternoon to determine what help could be sent to outlying communities where influenza cases were multiplying. But when the director of the Henry Street Nursing Service showed that the clouds were also gathering over New York, with some five hundred diagnosed cases of influenza reported within four days and many more as yet undiagnosed, those present, alarmed, immediately organized for relief in the city itself. To the request that I serve as chairman of the Nurses' Emergency Council, I acceded on condition that all nursing agencies coördinate and all clear through our nursing centres as the best organized to meet such an emergency. Before adjournment, the temporary Red Cross building on Fifth Avenue was turned over for our headquarters, and Mrs. Hermann Biggs and Mrs. Henry Goddard Leach agreed to start early the next morning to obtain the support of municipal and private agencies affiliated with the various social service groups. Catholics, Jews, and Protestants — all of them agreed to the plan. A form for a handbill was drawn up, and given to the printer in a small shop in the neighborhood of Henry Street. He worked all night to print these.

In the morning, dignified and discerning women stood on the steps at Altman's and Tiffany's Fifth Avenue shops and accosted passers-by. Before the day was half spent, hundreds of men and women came to the office to volunteer their services. At headquarters we were quick in sizing up, accepting, and assigning to their posts those who seemed competent.

A Stern Task for Stern Women

There is nothing in the epidemic of SPANISH INFLUENZA to inspire panic.

There is everything to inspire coolness and courage and sacrifice on the part of American women.

A stern task confronts our women--not only trained women, but untrained women.

The housewife, the dietitian, the nurses' aide, the practical nurse, the undergraduate nurse and the trained nurse herself-- all of these are needed.

Humanity calls them
Lives depend upon their answer

Capable, though untrained hands, can lighten the burden of the trained ones. There are many things intelligent women can do to relieve the situation, working under the direction of competent nurses.

Will you help do some of them?
Will you enroll for service Now?

If possible, apply personally at the New York County Chapter of the American Red Cross, 389 Fifth Avenue. Come prepared to fill out an enrollment blank like that printed below.

To physicians and to the nurse-employing public this appeal is made:

Unless it means life or death, please release for service all nurses attending chronic cases. Physicians should not employ nurses as office or laboratory assistants during this emergency.

Sample Enrollment Blank

Last name...First name ....
Residence....................................... ....Phone ....
Business address... Phone ....
Will serve (Hours).....................Days...................Weeks........................
Occupation ....
Will serve as volunteer.........................Will serve for pay........................

Nurses' Emergency
Council,
Lillian D. Wald, Chairman
Parmelia Doty, Exec, Secretary.

Countless illustrations could be given of the spirit of the city in the face of that desperate emergency. A telephone call came from Bellevue the first morning to say that the laundry staff, alarmed by the number of patients brought in every hour of the day and night, had abandoned the hospital. Before noon the domestic science instructors and students from Teachers College, Columbia University, were at work in their places. Throughout the days that followed there was impressive evidence of the willingness of people to help. Perhaps the spirit of service so often evidenced during the War held over. Two men who were assigned as orderlies to Welfare Island were old acquaintances of mine whose usual occupation was banking. On the other hand, a most indefatigable worker who could always be counted on I surmised to have been a prostitute. Her able service in one of our great hospitals won praise from the authorities and gratitude from the patients.

Public departments, social agencies, civic organizations, police, tenement house inspectors, nurses, nurses' aides, untrained volunteers, were knit into one great, flexible, interlocking mechanism, giving bedside care to the sick, supplying and distributing soup and custard, bed linen and night clothing, furnishing child care and housekeeping assistance, clearing records, running a motor service for almost every section of the city. Henry Street subdivided its staff into eight-hour shifts, sending out one squad at night and thus preventing the unmanageable accumulation in the morning. Automobiles and taxi service assisted in the night rounds. There was literally no duplication in the vast number of cases visited, and this despite the fact that in some instances as many as eleven, and in one case twenty-three, anxious people reported the same household. Complete coöperation was secured, and days passed before there was any tampering with the machinery. The record was marred by a well-intentioned group who wanted to help, but without gearing their efforts into the general scheme. The effectiveness of the organization may be seen in the fact that the morning after the disruption the chairman at headquarters was informed of the mistake and was able to trace the cause, and though the delicate machinery upon which so much depended was damaged, and doubt of its functioning was instilled, no breakdown occurred.

When the Nurses' Emergency Council disbanded after the epidemic was no longer a menace, an outline for after-care was asked for by the Commissioner of Health, and was accepted by him. The stations throughout the city were reëstablished to carry on their normal programmes, and staffs of health, welfare, and visiting nurse services were resumed as before.

This experience unforgettably impressed on many of us the fact that precious time and energy are wasted during ordinary periods, and, as well, the fact that the nurses appear to be the only groups highly organized and ready to step into a large-scale emergency. Another memorable lesson was that education which had been given to mothers and to fathers held over even into crucial times. Comforting indeed to the Henry Street nurses were the statements brought in by their colleagues that those families who had been under our care gave evidence of comparative composure and invariably were ready with towels, hot water, and the equipment available for the care which the patient required. And this was impressive because these teachings were the result of education given in the simplest manner possible, far removed from academic form.

Few people comprehend the abyss of ignorance of the most elementary facts and the limited vocabulary of those whose only reading is the tabloids. In such homes the mother must get her education through personal, understanding contact, and the nurse is peculiarly fitted to serve as her teacher. It is important for nurses, and for those who have the training of nurses in charge, to comprehend how factual must be the methods used. One does not have to look far for illustrations.

The superintendent of a babies' hospital telephoned one day asking that a nurse be dispatched to a given address. A child had been sent home from the hospital because it was feared that she had been too long in the atmosphere and that her best chance for survival lay outside the institution. It was explained that only a report was needed, as the mother had been given full instructions, including a demonstration of a bath. The Henry Street nurse found that the child had received no attention whatever, and needed immediate care, which she gave. She reproached the mother for having failed to follow the hospital instructions. Said the mother, "I know the baby should have baths and they did show me how. But I did not have a marble slab and I could n't get one anywhere!" To her, the unfamiliar (and unattainable) marble slab had been the alpha and omega of the prescribed technique.

The nurse is, in the first years, perplexing to these inexperienced women. A group on Cherry Street was heard discussing this new acquaintance. Said one, who had known in her old-country parish the kindness of the nuns, and was evidently puzzled because there was no evidence of religious persuasion, "I know what they are — they are sisters without religion."

But how quick are simple minds to catch the essence of a lesson, clearly presented, was shown by the comment of a neighbor who had been told of infections and the danger to all through the neglect of the individual: "I declare to goodness, it ain't safe to be selfish!"

One who has not lived through the rush of immigration, nor seen old customs and old superstitions apparently fixed in the minds as absolutes, cannot measure, as we do, the changes that have been wrought. Even now our nurses occasionally meet with instances such as this: —

Mrs. N., a young colored woman, the proud mother of a new baby boy, was being given care by the Henry Street nurse. Turning the patient over to finish her bath, she discovered, to her horror, that the patient had been lying on a long, sharp bread knife. The nurse, alarmed but successfully concealing her feelings, remarked, "I suppose you were cutting bread for the children and forgot about the knife." "Lawse, no, honey chile! I had right bad cramps las' night — and my gramma she done say there ain't nuttin' better than to lay on a long, sharp knife to cure dem dar crampin' after-pains. And Nurse, honey, I'se all better this mawnin'."

Dealing with people who hold to such superstitions as this, we often find ourselves baffled in our attempts to bring modern health methods to them. Fortunately there are incidents that keep up our faith. A year ago, when conscientious people were coöperating with the Department of Health in the effort to immunize the city against diphtheria, I chanced on one of our centres near Chatham Square, in the midst of a population little trained in the miracles of science. I had the great joy of witnessing that morning the effect of the teaching of the head nurse. This sympathetic woman quietly and calmly explained the purposes of the safeguarding injection, and there was one hundred per cent compliance of the mothers in the treatment — a miracle indeed.

The National Committee for Mental Hygiene, under Dr. Frankwood Williams, in generosity provided an expert Mental Hygiene Supervisor for the Henry Street staff. Mental hygiene within the last decade has acquired tremendous significance, and its application to public health nursing has placed in our hands an increasingly effective implement of education and help. Clifford Beers's recital [1] of his tragic experience has been quick to rouse sentiment and action. The first little group that met in New Haven, when Mr. Beers appeared and presented the subject as an obligation upon

[1] *A Mind That Found Itself.*

social workers, has grown into the present well-organized, stimulating, and effective National Committee for Mental Hygiene, with its far-reaching international affiliations. Miss Glee Hastings, loaned to us for a period of a year, is now a permanent member of our staff, making a significant contribution to our nurses' education. To her the nurse refers problem cases which occur in the families under care and for whom she needs further guidance. The story of Caroline is an example of one such problem: —

A nurse was called to the West Side, where a child had been burned. While she cared for her little patient, she heard moans and cries from the next room. Inquiring whether another member of the family was ill, she was told, "Oh, that is only Caroline. She cries like that every day. But you can go in if you like." The nurse found a twenty-year-old girl lying on the bed in a dark room, weeping. Three years before, she had worked in a piano factory, where she was very unhappy. She thought the other girls shunned her because of the acne on her face. One day, when she had arranged to lunch with two other girls, she saw them walking arm in arm. She was sure they were avoiding her because they thought her skin trouble was "not a nice one," as she put it. In despair, the poor creature flung herself out of a window. An awning broke the fall and she was unhurt, but she was sent home in an ambulance. At first she had only sympathy from her family, but nothing would induce her to go out. For three years she had retreated each day to the dark little bedroom as soon as the housework was done.

In all that time her mother had succeeded in persuading her to leave the house only once.

The nurse soon saw that Caroline's unemployment was serious to the household, and that her "stubbornness" was resented. The family impatience was intensified by the fact that the son of the house wanted to marry "his girl," and his wages could not be spared unless the sister went to work. The nurse shrewdly saw that the fiancée had the biggest stake in the situation. She found the latter coöperative, and, as she "lived at home," her time was her own. Tactfully, the suffering Caroline was persuaded to go to a skin clinic, on the understanding that her future sister-in-law would accompany her, wait for her during the treatment, and escort her home. When this programme was proceeding satisfactorily, the nurse took Caroline to a psychopathic clinic, where she found help of another kind. Next came the problem of a job for Caroline. A telephone switchboard position seemed the best. Her acne and her self-confidence had both improved, and the girl was sent to the Y.W.C.A. to learn her trade. When she was ready, the Settlement gave her a substitute place during vacation. With a month's experience and recommendation, Caroline secured a position with the New York Telephone Company. Recently, the joyous nurse responsible for the "treatment" gave me the cheering news that the brother is married and that Caroline has a "boy friend."

This is but one of the many instances of the newer opportunities which an understanding of mental hygiene gives. Without this broader outlook, the nurse might sometimes fail to meet an opportunity to give needed help because it seemed outside her nursing function. A Henry Street nurse was once called to Allen Street to attend a sick woman. When she arrived, less than an hour later, she found that the patient had died. The woman had been insane, but her husband had feared to report her, lest she be taken to the hospital. The father and a sweet young daughter sat in the kitchen, frightened and helpless. The nurse found the dead woman, unwashed, unclean, bedraggled, her nightgown torn to shreds. She felt deeply that the picture of the dead mother might be a haunting memory for the young girl to carry through life. With great care she washed the woman, combed and arranged the tangled hair, put decent garb upon her, and smoothed the bed before calling the young girl. In a narrow sense, this was not part of the nurse's function. But in a real sense she had a duty to that child, and she probably saved the girl a shock that would have scarred her irremediably.

The mental hygiene movement has profoundly affected the whole field of public health nursing. Twenty agencies during the last ten years have added mental hygiene consultants to their own staffs. Just as there has been growing recognition that it is impossible to separate social well-being — or lack of it — from physical health, so it is every day becoming clearer that in work with individuals and families, especially where contact is as close as with the public health nurse, consideration must be given to the emotional and mental make-up of the individual and the effect of family and other relationships on his total adjustment to life.

Furthermore, in the nurse's approach to her cases, she needs to know the fundamentals of modern psychology so that her own relationship to them may be sound and productive.

The last decade has seen the strengthening of the partnership between the professional and nonprofessional groups concerned with public health nursing — board and committee members and volunteers. This has led to a more widespread understanding of the public health programme on the part of the community, and also has developed a feeling of responsibility among interested citizens, though it is not as yet sufficiently comprehended.

While I have tried to indicate some of the achievements in nursing and health in recent years and to point out some of the most fruitful lines of effort, I must also show the reader at least one of the challenging problems in this field. As the tales in this book so often picture the tragedy of the birth of children under impoverished, almost hopeless family conditions, the question of the control and regulation of the size of the family must rise in the minds of many readers. It would be futile to attempt an adequate discussion here, for in a broad sense the question of increasing and decreasing birth and death rates belongs to the scientific study of population. There is a decrease of 128,000 children under five years of age shown in the last census of vital statistics of the United States, for a decade that showed a 17 per cent increase in the total population. The practice of contraception doubtless plays its part in the trend reflected in these figures. If voluntary regulation of families is repellent, and if on the other hand a diminishing population is a matter of concern, would it not be logical to assist large families financially so that the full burden would not fall on those who are unable to do justice to the numerous children and to the overtaxed mother? This theme is too involved and too controversial for me to do more than suggest in this place the many questions which rise for debate out of the 1930 Census figures and out of the evidence reported by social workers. The horizon clearly indicates that discussion and measures to handle the problem by sound and ethical means are bound to come.

It would be impossible to measure the advances that have been made without a thrilling sense of enlarged opportunity and the successful realization of what might have seemed an impossible vision. In realizing its aims, public health nursing owes an unpayable debt to that great foundation which has instigated and supported the aspirations of the nurses and their colleagues in medicine and in other fields of constructive health. The Rockefeller Report for 1930 describes visits and surveys by its staff members in China, Japan, the Philippine Islands, Straits Settlements, Siam, India, Egypt, Palestine, Syria, Turkey, Austria, Bulgaria, Czechoslovakia, England, France, Germany, Greece, Italy, Norway, Poland, Yugoslavia, Canada, and the United States. Through its Associate Director of Studies, the gifted and tactful Mary Beard, it has invited experienced nurses to visit centres where services have been newly established, and has given fellowships for the training of supervisors and administrators. Training schools have been organized with its aid in numerous communities where the need for them is acute.

As this chapter is primarily designed to do no more than indicate the origin and development of the nursing and health efforts as seen from Henry Street, it cannot, of course, be a complete report of them, but such information is readily available for those who desire detailed data.

I have omitted much that would show how a nursing service, when motivated by the social urge, develops its own and related fields of help.   In *The House on Henry Street* [2] the beginnings of numerous experiments were told.   The service of the nurse, the obligations of which are indicated in the title we assumed, "Public Health Nurse," and which won the cherished valuation from Dr. Welch, has spread over our country — over the greater part of the globe. Our first successful efforts to reach the children in the schools are now an accepted practice throughout the country. The suggestion to the Metropolitan Life Insurance Company to provide nursing care for its industrial policyholders has been widely extended. It is now accepted by the John Hancock Insurance Company for their industrial policyholders, and many employers, public and private, make similar provision for their employees.

Industrial hygiene is largely under the care of the public health nurse. It is more generally established in other communities than our own, and will probably

[2] By Lillian D. Wald, 1915.

increase. But there is much more to be done. Further coördination must be found between the various measures already established. The pioneers have begun the work; it is far from finished. New fields, new enterprises, are visible. The times call for the high spirit of the courageous pioneers among physicians, scientists, and nurses.

The purpose and the performance of the entire movement are, I think, crystallized in the dedication carved in the mantel of our Central Administration Building: —

THIS BUILDING IS GIVEN IN MEMORY OF
JACOB HENRY SCHIFF
BY THERESE, HIS WIFE,
AND IS DEDICATED TO THE CAUSE OF PUBLIC HEALTH NURSING
WHICH HE LONG FOSTERED FOR LOVE OF PROGRESSIVE
EDUCATION,
CIVIC RIGHTEOUSNESS AND MERCIFUL MINISTRATION.

That dedication constitutes a pledge and a prophecy. The service, fully comprehended, demands no less.

VI

GIVERS AND THEIR GIFTS

HOMER, who sang of many things that are still timely, observed that "A timid man makes a poor beggar." Modern begging is quite different from what it was in the days when the hungry were fed from the kitchen plenty, but we know to-day, as Homer knew, that he who asks in the name of charity must be prepared to ask with intelligence and persistence.

Twentieth-century business terms seem not at all unsuitable for the modern practice of this very ancient calling. "Have you sold the idea?" is frequently the question of the super-salesmen who organize the "drives" to secure funds from willing — often very willing — givers. Scrutiny of to-day's technique reveals neither whining nor camouflage, but the inventiveness and efficiency of the age. That the American public is willing to give is more than proved by the estimate that annual benefactions exceed two billion dollars. There are, however, even in our complex modern life, examples of the old simple method of enlisting interest merely by the telling of the tale. That was Henry Street's happy experience up to the time when our annual budget totaled a hundred and fifty thousand dollars. We permitted no solicitation, and no "benefits" were given. The appearance of the nurses proclaimed their mission. People were told of conditions, by what measures we were trying to improve them; they responded to their own impulses and gave the necessary money. But beyond that point organization set in. And now, when I describe our work, almost inevitably the question comes, "How do you get your money?"

This is not unnatural, since the annual budget has reached almost a million dollars. In answering, one is tempted to give first place to the generous, often sacrificial gifts of people of small means, and to emphasize these for their human significance, beyond even the essential contributions of the wealthy and the large appropriations of farseeing foundations.

A Negro was asked to give a dollar for the nursing service, but he brought ten dollars instead of one. Knowing the man's situation, one of the workers protested, "Oh, that 's too much!"

"Yes, ma'am, it may seem to you a dollar is right," he replied; "but my heart tells me ten dollars."

One evening there was a knock at the door which

Florence Kelley answered. A stranger, tired, shabby, stood before her.

"Is this the house that's good to all nations?" he asked.

"Yes, I think it is," said Mrs. Kelley.

"Well," said the man, "I've brought it a dollar."

He would n't come in. He had walked weary miles from West 23rd Street to Henry Street. He did not want his name known. We never saw him again, never knew who he was.

I. Goldberg kept a "family liquor store," and his kindly wife gave wine to any sick woman whose need was brought to her attention. After her death he came to us.

"I used to enjoy those customers so much," he said. "Can't you get me some more? I miss not giving to them." He continued to call now and then, and we were soon well acquainted. One day he came for advice on a knotty point. He had hoped to give to the White House a very beautiful bronze statue, the work of a countryman of his. The statue depicted a supposedly motherless baby, held in the arms of a helpless father. It had been delicately intimated that his gift might not be acceptable because of his "family liquor store." I took advantage of his visit to ask for help in selecting a suitable location on our street for a blind jeweler, whose trade-union had contributed a hundred dollars, Henry Street having secured a like sum. My caller's immediate response was, "I'll give fifty dollars!"

"I should be glad to have that addition to my neighbor's capital," I said, "but you came to me for a favor.

I hesitate to accept the gift, under the circumstances. But," I quickly added, "if when you return home you have not changed your mind, please send the money."

"You are wrong," said Mr. I. Goldberg. "The me that wants to give you the fifty dollars is the real me. If I go home my sons may say, 'Father, we cannot afford so much,' and I might send you twenty-five dollars. Please let me be the real me."

He handed me a check then and there.

And I treasure the letter from a woman who wrote: "I see in the papers that you need money. You took care of my little boy when he was so bad burned and all my life since then I pray God, make me rich so I can help you big. But he hasn't answered my prayer so I send this which I know isn't much but it is all I have." With the letter was enclosed a ten-dollar bill.

It is hard to know whether to laugh or to weep over those who, poor in money but rich in good will, have given what they held most dear.

Sometimes when the night is long with sleepless worry, I remember the hysterical woman in a near-by tenement who did not mind dragging me out at all hours. But she was a grateful patient, and when she died she left me her most precious possession, a cabinet photograph of her deceased husband.

And there was Maggie Lynch's bequest. Maggie Lynch lived in a converted loft on Grand Street. She was born with the deformity of a stump instead of a full-length arm, to which was grown a miniature hand. But her "little hand," as she called it, was useful to Maggie, because with it she could wring out the clothes. When she was sixteen, Maggie was invited to the Street Car Conductors' Ball, a special invitation from a lodger in the Lynches' loft. Maggie must not go, without an arm like other girls. Her godmother, a hard-working, warm-hearted charwoman, called to enlist our help in securing the artificial substitute for Maggie's calamitous need. Tiemann, New York's leading manufacturer of artificial limbs, agreed to make the arm and hand at a great reduction, but even so it would cost a round sum. This the godmother paid.

The great day came when Maggie was to have her arm, and I accompanied her to pass upon the workmanship. As we walked home I tried tactfully to disregard the new member, but this, I soon found, was all wrong. The artificial arm was the most expensive thing any Lynch had ever owned. Maggie stopped to show it to every acquaintance we passed. When finally we reached her home, Maggie paraded between the washtubs and the littered table in the Lynch kitchen, with a shawl draped like a long skirt, practising the management of a train with her new arm and hand. Maggie, we heard, was quite the belle of the Conductors' Ball.

But Henry Street was by no means through with Maggie's arm. For the poor girl contracted tuberculosis and died. She lay in her satin-lined coffin, the arm conspicuously displayed. As I looked upon her, the mother whispered, "Miss Wald, one of the last things Maggie said was, you was to have that arm.

As soon as ever the wake is over and the casket closed, we 'll be sending it to you."

The arm arrived at 4 A.M., wrapped in a newspaper. We put it high on a closet shelf, but every time the closet was cleaned there was a shriek — that arm had fallen on someone. It got on our nerves so many times that finally we buried Maggie's arm in our little back yard. But a greyhound, a temporary resident, retrieved it, and laid it proudly at the feet of a distinguished visitor who was being shown the garden. Then we knew that something final would have to be done with Maggie's arm. It was made into a neat parcel and returned to the makers. They gave us $2.34, which was added to the budget for relief.

"Campaigns" carried on to raise funds are often painful crucifixion to those who are so personally involved. We have a great solace in the generosity of our neighbors, and in the strong support of young people and of groups within the House, who not only give, but do the much more difficult thing of asking others to give.

But seeking help for a cherished object is not wholly without pleasurable satisfaction. The power to transmit faith in a cause, to stir response, to change inattention or indifference to active participation, and not infrequently to arouse a readiness to sacrifice leisure, amusement, money, richly repays any strain of effort and emotion.

The history of this period will not be told in full unless place of honor is given to the people who, having made their money, care deeply that it be spent for constructive, remedial programmes and measures. It would take many pages to enumerate the individuals and the groups who give with wisdom. One thinks immediately of the vast purpose of the Rockefeller Foundation, which works unceasingly for the eradication of disease the world over, knowing no racial or religious barrier — and that is entirely appropriate, since germs themselves have no frontiers. One thinks, too, of the Julius Rosenwald Fund, which, among impressive benefactions, singled out the urgent needs of the Negro; and of the Milbank Memorial Fund, which has furthered so many efforts in the fields of education and public health.

Anyone who knows intimately of givers whose interest ranges, as did that of Jacob H. Schiff, from bicycles for small boys or a suitable stand for a news dealer to large allocations to organized efforts and to universities must have been impressed by the wisdom that distinguishes between what should be given and what withheld out of deference to some subtle dignity. Thus a radical socialist organization, carrying on workers' education, once asked for help which Mr. Schiff confided to me he would gladly have given, for he felt that America's future rests on the intelligence of the workers. But he thought it unwise for that group to take money from him; it was bound to lead to misunderstanding, just as he would have been misunderstood had he given it.

I have come in contact with the very conscientious givers, who displayed in their giving their sense of personal obligation, their intelligent comprehension of needs, and who have had breadth in their vision. Such men and women have grown to feel personal public and collective responsibility, which has not infrequently been expressed in support of institutions that do not represent their own religious or political faith.

I know the Jew who gave money for the erection of a shrine dear to the hearts of a community of Catholics; and the Protestant who was among the first to encourage the building and who gave support to Clinton Hall, which was designed, among other things, to provide a dignified place for the religious festivals of the Jews of our neighborhood.

A man who has a place among the more conservative bankers willingly put in the hands of Josephine Roche a goodly sum for her notable experiment based on active coöperation with organized labor in her Colorado coal mines. He knew that at the time local bankers denied her credit because of her unorthodox industrial procedure, and that other mine owners in the area were leagued against her. Nor was this banker the only New York capitalist who, holding conservative economic views, nevertheless came to her support.

On Henry Street we have had wonderful experience in generosity and encouragement from people who disagreed with us on measures which had enlisted our support. Some of them saw in our programme an insurance against reckless reliefs not thoroughly thought through: Henry Street workers were termed "practical idealists." There is, as a wise modern philosopher has pointed out, a great need for people who are "divinely practical and not stupidly so."

On the other hand, I could cite instances of givers whose generosity toward the poverty-stricken or the afflicted disappeared when they found themselves in personal disagreement — economic or political — with a leader in the enterprise. Though our own efforts have been so kindly regarded, we have had agonizing experiences of help given and then withdrawn. It would seem worth recording that the reason has never been disapproval of the work, but rather criticism of the head worker. This we experienced first when a small fund was withdrawn because I supported a cloak makers' strike. There was no question of the validity of the strikers' claims, but by espousing their cause I put myself outside the pale. Another offense was the posting at the Settlement of a plea for equal suffrage. The writer of a letter which was notice of withdrawal of funds reminded us that the money for the support of the Settlement came from those who opposed suffrage as well as those who favored it. Sympathy with the Lawrence textile strike brought disapproval, and a salary for a nurse was withdrawn because of my affiliation with the Progressive Party. The argument ran like this: the money had been given because of the donor's faith in my judgment; but by going on the Committee for Legislative Reform of the Progressive Party I destroyed that faith. We paid for my pacifism, too — my passionate desire to have people care for each other as a basis for ending war was oddly construed as lack of patriotism. The frank statement of principles was at a cost to the Settlement's work. And a readiness to encourage impartial study of the

Russian Revolution at the Settlement scored heavily against us.

Terence MacSwiney, whose death in prison as the result of a hunger strike gives him place among the Irish martyrs, had once been a guest at the Settlement. The memory of that visit brought to us his sisters when they came to America to testify to the political situation at home. Tragic they seemed to us, and our hospitality to them was no more than a gesture of kindliness. And yet at a meeting the next day of a group with money to give, this matter was brought up as of serious import, and a fund, the allocation of which was under discussion, was not given to the nursing service. I am sure the veto vote was not carefully considered, but such slight incidents do often determine the maintenance of good causes.

The act of disapproval most painful to us brought the withdrawal of a large yearly appropriation which had made possible essential work for the Negroes.

On the other hand, Henry Street has had generous and unfailing support from many people who differed, but who in unmistakable terms declared that freedom of opinion and sincere practice can never be discordant. Not a few gifts have come to the Settlement in recognition of what the givers approved as "a courageous stand."

Though large gifts have enabled the work to expand, and have served many causes in making Henry Street a demonstration centre, its influence unlimited by boundaries of geography, occasional unhappy incidents sometimes distort the picture of the American giver and his unmatched generosity. I for one would testify that the impulse of the donor is usually disinterested and far-reaching, though his gift is not always based upon careful reasoning or inquiry into actual situations.

A study of wills is in itself educational. The lawyers who are advisers to the testators must share some of the responsibility. Not a few of them have agreed that they themselves are to blame for what might in all charity be called absurd bequests. The will of the late Ella Wendel has been a most striking example. This woman of almost incredibly narrow experience left enormous sums of money to outdated and remote needs. Indeed, the gifts in some instances are said by those close to the intended beneficiaries to be an embarrassment.

Within a year a round sum was stated in the papers to have been given for a horse trough beside a Long Island road that is now a crowded motor highway. Such old bequests are frozen — there is no way of carrying out the kindly intent of the giver, and to divert the money to more timely purposes is a complicated legislative process. One of the wealthiest communities near New York City was given the interest from a large fortune to care for "decayed gentlewomen who have supported themselves by the needle," though none are now found in what has grown in half a generation from a simple country town to a rich and sophisticated suburb.

The Community Trust, in calling attention to the fact that well-intentioned bequests sometimes fail because there are no beneficiaries within their terms, cites the classic case of Benjamin Franklin's legacy for the aid of "indentured apprentices," who are no longer to be found in America. A bequest by a former mayor of St. Louis for the benefit of "those who travel in covered wagons" is also cited. And the Samaritan Female Society provided a century ago a fund to be administered by the Andover Theological Seminary for the purchase of red flannels for the "bodily comfort" of theological students. Andover Seminary is no longer at Andover, and taste and comfort now prescribe other underwear. But it has taken an order of the court to make the fund available for the medical care and nursing of indigent students.

The question has been brought up of the obligation of the attorney to study for his client the validity of philanthropic institutions and efforts, the same sort of responsibility that a careful lawyer would assume if his client proposed to make investments of doubtful security. At the first Children's Conference called by Theodore Roosevelt during his presidency, there was unanimity from East and West and North and South, from Catholics, Jews, and Protestants, from all agencies interested in children, that institutional life is not desirable for the young, that the fatherless child is best protected if the mother and the home are made secure, and that a foster home is usually the best provision for the orphan. But it is amazing how rare is the philanthropist who gives largely to measures for education and help in the home. Leaders in the medical profession, particularly the pediatricians, have long de-

THE CARPENTRY SHOP

clared the disadvantages of institutional care for children, sick or well. The nurses who go into the homes, who are recognized as educators as well as "good angels" to the sick, carry a great and undisputed appeal, but they encounter surprising difficulties in securing money to make possible their good work, which rests in almost all instances upon a hazardous financial basis.

For a number of years vast resources have been used for social research. Some of it has been expensively and almost aimlessly entered into, and nothing was gained through the findings. This is sometimes due to the fact that the circumstances leading to an elaborate inquiry have changed by the time the study is finished. To the practical worker, seeking for immediate relief from conditions that make the day, the month, the season, almost unendurable, research seems at times a hindrance rather than a source of help. Every busy desk receives countless questionnaires, though with the depression the amount of research and the number of researchers have somewhat fallen off. The factors upon which wide social progress is based require time and care and accuracy. I doubt whether the percentage of returns received, or their quality, warrants the weighty deductions, unless the study complies with high standards of scholarly inquiry.

There is, of course, serious and responsible research that can and often does settle disturbing questions. There are accurate and scientific research workers, whose standards of integrity are unassailable. Probably the most impressive are the famous foundations' study of disease, and the inquiry into the cost of medical care in American communities. These have definite objectives, and the facts are ascertained and interpreted only by trained investigators. As I travel around the world I find, even in remote centres, general understanding that the people responsible for these studies are concerned with humanity and not with politics or self-gain.

Some part of the dissatisfaction with social research in general is doubtless to be traced to the seekers after the Ph.D. degree, some of whom spend time and effort restating the known on the basis of "original investigation." Many of us join heartily with Sir Arthur Salter, who stated before the Conference of Universities, "I do not advocate cessation of scientific research or technical training, but the proper use of the gifts of science is now more important than their increase."

Thoughtful parents and wise teachers have, I think, always recognized the need of stimulating the child to give. The habit must be acquired very early or this lovable impulse will be inhibited. A nurse relates the attitude of one small boy whose family talked freely about "impostors" who asked help of which they were not really in need. The little lad was recovering from a contagious disease and one of his limited amusements was to look out of the window. One day an organ grinder with a gayly clad monkey came down the street, the monkey holding out a tiny red cap. The little convalescent had a good many pennies, and his nurse suggested that the monkey would probably be very glad to have a coin or two in his cap. The little sophisticate replied that he did n't think the monkey needed any, he was so well dressed.

Such an example is, of course, rare as compared with the child who wants to give and who should be encouraged to do so, though it is not easy to help the child who has plenty to escape a sense of superiority to the other who, through no fault of his own, lacks money, presentable clothes and shoes, and the means of getting into the country even for two weeks in the summer.

People are stirred to give sometimes by compunctions, sometimes by treasured memories, sometimes by the broadest conception of the responsibility of human beings toward one another. Some are born with a desire to help; some must have training and stimulus. One wealthy man lamented the fact that he had not the instinct to give, that he envied those who could give without pressure, sometimes self-imposed; and I think this quality should not be forgotten by those who take seriously the culture of children. One family of close friends grew anxious over the unwillingness of a very young member, aged four, to share her toys. "For," said they, "she will have a very dull and uninteresting life if she does n't overcome that characteristic."

I am not oblivious of the fact that men and women sometimes are thought to give time or money to philanthropic enterprises in part, at least, to further social ambitions. There is no circle to which that practice is confined. The telegraph "boy" who once brought a message late at night I recognized as a friend of long ago. He tarried to tell me of the family we had once known. "All was well with my brother-in-law till he was ruined by charity," he said. Thinking this would prove to be an incident of unwisely bestowed benefactions, I inquired further.

"It just began this way. We moved to Chicago, and he had a little business which he knew how to run; and everybody in the family helped him. And then he gave some money to a charity and the charity people asked him to go on a committee, and he worked something fierce for that committee. And then they asked him to go on another and he was very proud, and would you believe it, they asked him to go on a third. He gave a little money to each committee, and that was all right. But he neglected his business. Now he has only two people working for him instead of seven, and he don't make much, and that's how charity ruined him."

In the giving of money there is scope for an awareness of complexities and the highest kind of statesmanship. While one values an emotional reaction, there is at the same time a desire, not for hesitation in giving, but for intelligent appreciation of how and when and where to give. The director of every important organization is sometimes faced with the obligation of advising against giving money to his or her precious undertaking. Familiarity with causes and needs at times makes it necessary to lay before the giver other opportunities more immediately urgent than the requirements of one's own programme. The Settlement has never regretted taking that course, and in the end has never suffered because of it. When a gift was once offered us for tubercular patients, we felt it imperative to tell of a momentarily more pressing need for that exact sum which had come to our attention. Unless the amount was made available, an institution caring for tubercular patients with signal success would be unable to continue through the winter. We told the story, and the money offered us was diverted to save that project. When the giver described the situation to her wise attorney, he was sufficiently impressed to advise his client to appropriate a more adequate sum, on an annual basis, to Henry Street.

In giving, as in other fields, the times call for a broad comprehension of how the underprivileged can best be protected and wisely helped in a way to stimulate, not retard, their own development. One of the great lessons of the depression is that the government must take more responsibility for social welfare, though we have a long road to travel before public relief alone is sufficient or even desirable. Satisfactory human relations are built upon expressions of compassion, of understanding, of willingness to help, and upon the recognition of the fact that we are all interrelated as human beings.

Private gifts are as essential to practical programmes as to the spiritual needs of those who give and those who receive. It is impossible to wait upon government appropriations for all the emergencies that clamor at the door. Perhaps the giving of money and with it the acceptance of social responsibility by the government are most encouragingly exemplified in widows' pensions and old-age pensions.

In the poorest neighborhoods the gifts of the poor to one another can never be set down in dollars and cents. All of us know neighbors who have taken in another family or an unemployed relative or friend. The clubs whose members have the most meagre financial resources never fail to respond to an appeal by one of their own members to help another known to be in need. I have seen everyone in a tenement house contribute toward getting "the professor" for a sick child whom they hoped the miracle-working physician could help. Such occurrences are less frequent in these depression years, but though the resources of all are nearly minus, the spirit remains the same.

The community trust funds that make incomes available for current uses serve great ends. But to safeguard their highest purpose it is important that the trustees should include men and women, particularly women, who are familiar with social needs and with the best agencies; execution should not be limited to people whose experience has been mainly confined to finance. It is equally important that the trustees be guarded against yielding to the clamor for new and untried ventures while proved services are handicapped or even suspended because of lack of support; at the same time, the trustees should not be timid about encouraging fresh experiments by courageous pioneers which offer reasonable promise of usefulness. My experience indicates that on the whole the money turned over to organizations for their work is carefully and thriftily expended. There has been training in conservation through the years.

But the form of giving — trust, endowment, foundation, detailed bequest, or whatever is chosen — cannot preserve the values of the most generous impulse to give if the donor fails in forethought and study. Many times it has seemed necessary to remind a giver that if he (almost always he) intended to make an investment in mining, railroads, real estate, the contract would never be signed without expert opinion on the project. And yet this same cautious business man will give for philanthropic purposes thousands — sometimes millions — without seeking informed guidance.

From a wealth of available illustrations, let me cite the enormous gifts of a man who made his fortune in chocolate candy. His purpose was to create and endow an orphan asylum, though educators and social workers have long declared such institutions outmoded, behind the knowledge and the needs of the times. The gift, fifty years ago, might have served a most appealing purpose. But circumstances have changed; we have come to emphasize the nurture and education of the child as an individual rather than the child as a unit in a collective home, and the intended benefaction was signally open to the criticism it received.

Thus Homer Folks, secretary of the New York State Charities Aid Society, and twice president of the National Conference of Social Work, pointed out, in an interview published by the *New York Evening Post*, "The general opinion is that children should be helped at home when possible, that home care is better

than any substitute, and that the kind of specialized
education which the Hershey Industrial School con-
templates should be made available to all children suitable therefor through the public and other schools,
and without being coupled with free support in an
institution and with isolation from the surviving parent. To have to give up a mother, to all intents and
purposes, after having lost a father, is a pretty high
price to pay for admission into even the best institution."

And Mr. Folks further commented, "What a magnificent work could have been done by Mr. Hershey's
gift ($60,000,000) had it been devoted to preventive
work for the diminution of orphanage, for the assist-
ing of children in their own homes in case of need,
for the promotion of child health by all the ways which
are now known to be so effective!"

Philanthropy, like all other manifestations of will
and good will, is not static. Times change, needs modify, standards alter. Attitudes of privileged men and
women move toward a conception of new opportunities for the underprivileged. There is a science of giving, and a science of receiving. And the good impulse
to give is perhaps more general in the United States
than in any other country in the world. Generosity is an
American creed. Much is given with trained thought
and realization of the consequences of the money bestowed, but not all the lessons of wise giving have been
learned. On the basis of forty years' acquaintance and
study, this is how I see American givers: emotional,
statesmanlike, lavish, narrow, inclined to follow a pat-
tern, and sometimes most imaginative and venturesome.

VII

EDUCATION AND THE ARTS

At the Settlement, education in its broadest implication engages our attention first, last, and all the time. There is no limit to our concept of education. We long for a new definition which will give appraisal to the values that are not merely the passing on of instruction, which will recognize, as we recognize, that all such procedures as make up our programmes — summer and winter, in town and in country — are truly educational. All that we undertake for the neighborhood, and particularly for the children, has been planned with a sense of its social importance.

We believe that education must begin before the child enters the world, through instruction of the mother, that he may be as well born as is possible under the circumstances of environment and inheritance. The potentialities here are far greater than the unfamiliar observer can realize.

When to this we add elements which contribute to life's beauty and richness, — music, drama, handicrafts, gentle manners, cleanliness and order, organized family mealtimes, — we are offering education in the things of the spirit, making for a broader humanity.

It was, of course, inevitable that we should take a vital interest in the education offered the children of the city through the public schools. We sought opportunities, and opportunities sought us, for ways of helpful coöperation between the Settlement and the schools. Some of these I have described elsewhere;[1] others have developed in the years since 1915, the time with which this book is primarily concerned.

One of the closest bonds between Henry Street and the schools in the past two decades has been the Ungraded Classes. To use the nurses' vernacular, we were called in at the birth of this movement, we followed its growth from year to year, and Elizabeth Farrell, its creator, was a beloved resident of the House for nearly a quarter of a century.

The first beginnings of the Ungraded Classes go back to an earlier time. We were urging alumnæ of the established colleges to take the examinations and find places for themselves in the public school system. We believed such a contact between these graduates and an immigrant population would work wonders for both, and the few who heeded our plea made good in

[1] *The House on Henry Street*, by Lillian D. Wald.

many ways. One of these, a resident of the House, brought the glad tidings that there was a young teacher in her school who had "an idea." "The girl," she submitted, "needed looking after," as if having "an idea" laid her open to study, if not suspicion. This was our introduction to Elizabeth Farrell, the girl with "the idea." And when she had shared it with us it was borne in upon us that she had been vouchsafed a vision, though not till later was it developed by study and experience into the programme which has been praised and followed by educators the world over.

At that time we were unacquainted with the terms "I.Q.," "mental measurement," and "child guidance," so widely known now that they are familiar to the least sophisticated. Indeed, so easily do scientific words become slogans that we were amused, but not surprised, when a mother, uneducated by school or by life's experience, met a charge that she was responsible for her boy's truancy with a shrug and the remark, "I should worry. Ain't his I.Q. O.K.?"

Miss Farrell's "idea" was that *every* individual should be developed to the highest level of which he was capable. This was no startlingly new concept: Miss Farrell's originality lay in applying the idea to the education of the atypical in the public schools. She was optimistic enough to believe that the largest and most complex school system in the country, — perhaps in the world, — with its hundreds of thousands of children, its rigid curriculum, its mass methods, could be modified to meet the needs of the atypical — often the least lovely and potentially the most troublesome of its pupils. It is one of the priceless experiences of my life to have participated, even slightly, in this new formulation, and to have known the exaltation of its creator, which the hard experiences of a pioneer through the years were powerless to lessen.

With the approval of the principal of Public School Number 1, on Henry Street, Miss Farrell selected from its "chronic truants" the members of the first Ungraded Class in any public school system in the world. There were said to be at that time fifty thousand truants in New York City, boys and girls who had set themselves in opposition to society. Miss Farrell held that the children who were unwilling to attend school constituted a challenge to our whole scheme of public education; for she knew that this was not a problem peculiar to New York City — "it is doubtless the same in every city, in every town, perhaps in every village."

These subnormal and occasionally supernormal children were in the regular grades. They were getting little or no profit from their attendance, and held back their classmates who approached "the norm." Miss Farrell's experiment was based upon her certainty that the reason these atypical children played truant was that there was nothing which attracted them in the school. The docks, the streets, the empty lots, even the ash cans and the garbage, provided them with interest, if not education, as our elaborate school system failed to do. Miss Farrell discarded the old routine and brought into the classroom the materials, or their equivalent, that absorbed the boys and girls outside. In her hands, tin cans, picture puzzles, paints and brushes, wood and tools, became implements of education. Her children brought food to school and a luncheon was served — the first, so far as I know, in a city schoolroom. Friends of the Settlement gave pretty dishes and other necessary equipment, and the mothers were invited to visit the class, sometimes to take lunch. When an Italian mother was asked to prepare spaghetti for the children "like the old country," it dignified Italian parentage and custom in the eyes of these on-coming American citizens. We often overlook how important it is for children to hold to their traditions. Sometimes their loyalty and respect are greatly imperiled by the appeals to be "one hundred per cent Americans."

Before long the help of the specially trained physician was needed, and immediate response came from Dr. Adolf Meyer, then at Cornell, now distinguished for his work in psychiatry at Johns Hopkins. Psychiatry was not a word that had made its way into school parlance at that time. Doubtless the data sent to the interested and sympathetic expert from the Ungraded Class in Number 1 helped build up our reliance on the trained psychiatrist in dealing with "the problem child."

Miss Farrell's preparation for her chosen work was enlarged by visits to institutions for the feeble-minded in this country, in England and Scotland, and by further study at Jena. She was untiring in her effort to equip herself for the task she had undertaken.

Two members of the Board of Education — Charles Burlingham, the president, and Felix Warburg, his friend and colleague — were invited to meet Miss Farrell at Henry Street. In that sympathetic environment she forgot her shyness and presented her idea with glowing vigor and enthusiasm. With the superintendent of schools, Dr. Maxwell, one of the educational statesmen of the day, these socially minded board members paid tribute to her as a genius whose vision was essentially practical. She was given freedom and thoughtful encouragement to develop her project.

The position of Inspector of Ungraded Classes was created for Miss Farrell in 1906. She was before long regarded as an authority, in America and abroad, on educational methods for this type of pupil. I shall not attempt to follow the developments of the department through the years, its steady growth from the first experimental class to the important department it became. Neither can I particularize the advanced ideas and methods in testing and measuring the children, in the plan of study, in the organization of the work, which found their way into other public school rooms through the doorway of the Ungraded Classes.

A distinguished English authority who studied our public school system declared that the fact that this innovation could be introduced into a politically controlled city might be perplexing, but was certainly a dazzling demonstration of the power of a gifted and consecrated educator. The Board of Education deserves high praise for supporting this experiment.

Current statistics show that the Ungraded Classes have five hundred teachers, psychologists, and social workers, with nearly fifteen thousand handicapped or maladjusted children in their care.   A special building has been provided for the psycho-educational clinic, where educational therapy may be given to meet physical, mental, moral, and emotional needs.   New York's example has been followed by practically every large city in the United States.

If we in the Settlement share the pride of the public school authorities in this achievement, it is not only because we have been close to it throughout its growth, but because Elizabeth Farrell insisted that she found in the House a living spring of inspiration.   The Settlement's rich understanding of people, life, events, its multicolored and changing activities, provided her, she said, with a background which helped keep her own thought and emotions fresh and vital.   She never considered herself the dynamo that generated the power for her great achievement, though she had the unusual experience of recognition by colleagues in many fields. Professor Edward L. Thorndike testifies to his indebtedness to her when she was teaching a course at Teachers College, Columbia University: —

She never forgot that schools do not exist chiefly to serve some vague doctrine of education or some abstract ideal of the state, but must make life happier for actual living children in school and through life.   She was the defender of the interests of dull, thwarted, imperfect children whom she loved.

But I must share with the reader some of my intimate memories of my friend, and the stories that give a clue to the way she handled her problems.   It was one of our household pleasantries to say that no one who was not a "mongolian" [2] had her complete affection.

To illustrate the influence of teachers upon children, Miss Farrell loved to tell how from her Henry Street window she overheard one Sunday morning the play of a seven-year-old girl on the fire escape of the opposite tenement. The child was playing school, and she was the teacher. All the morning she kept it up, giving arithmetic lessons, marching the children downstairs for recess. "Left, right, left, right," she marked the time with her own feet. Commenting on personal appearance: "What a lovely hair ribbon you have, Minnie"; expressing annoyance where she felt it was due: "Did n't I tell you to keep the line straight!" And so on, and so on. One could hear the very tones of the teacher's voice. A little boy on the next fire escape was fascinated. "What's your name?" he called out. "Miss Thompson," the child interrupted herself long enough to reply. "Aw, I mean what's your name when you ain't the teacher?" But she was too busy settling a quarrel between two interesting incorrigibles to hear him.

And there was John, in that first class in Number 1 — John, who successfully resisted all efforts to improve his writing until Miss Farrell's ingenuity and the co-operation of the principal broke down the barriers. The children were encouraged to write to the principal when they had finished a particularly good piece of work, inviting him to come to see it. John wrote several such letters, but in his visits to the classroom

[2] The technical name for a hopeless feeble-minded type.

the principal never glanced toward the boy. At last it was too much to be borne longer in silence, and one day when the principal was in the room, admiring the work done by another pupil, John burst forth, "Yeh, you look at what everybody else does, but you don't pay no attention to my letters." "Why, John," was the reply, "were those your letters? I could n't read them." The little episode brought writing down to earth so far as John was concerned.

Also in that first class were Izzie and Giovanni, who quarreled one long day and made confusion in the classroom, and it was all about God. Izzie's God was Izzie's, and Giovanni's was Giovanni's. So their teacher asked Izzie to bring his Bible to school the next day, promising to bring a New Testament herself. The next day Izzie came with a big Bible written in Hebrew. He and the teacher compared selected passages from their Scriptures, line by line, verse by verse, until at last Izzie's prejudice could no longer hold up, and he said generously, "Well, I guess it 's the same God."

There came a day during the War when a whole public school received membership in the Junior Red Cross because of the work done by the Ungraded Class in that school in making and sending to France baby layettes, toys, and children's dresses. Elizabeth Farrell was bursting with pride when the Ungraded Class was honored in Assembly for the credit it had brought the school.

Nobody enjoyed more than Miss Farrell the humorous incidents that cropped up so often in her work, and the humor was not less appreciated when directed

toward herself.   She liked to tell of a little girl who
refused to talk, both at home and at school.   It is easy
to imagine the time and thought that went into the
effort to set the child right.   At last her impediment
gave way.   Later, when her speech was no longer
a new story, the child called upon Miss Farrell and
confided that her world was not rosy.   "Now I'm
talking," she said, "nobody wants to listen to me."

John H. Finley, who had watched Miss Farrell's work
and knew her well, summarizes her qualities in the
memorial tablet at the Oswego State Normal and Training School, of which she was an honored alumna: —

> Elizabeth Farrell
> who gave her life
> that the least might
> live as abundantly as
> their handicaps of
> mind or body permitted.
> A teacher
> of the atypical, the
> subnormal, the dull
> of spirit, the slow
> of speech, the inert;
> in teaching them
> she also gave in-
> struction in the
> method by which
> the normal, the
> bright and alert,
> should be taught.
> Beginning
> with a little group

of boys in the lower
East Side of Manhattan,
she became the tutelary of
the ungraded classes for
all New York, deeming
no child too atypical
to be neglected.

Elizabeth Farrell had another side, not known to many of her co-workers — her deep understanding of poetry and the classics, her knowledge of Oriental rugs, Chinese pottery, Japanese prints, old furniture, rare books. She herself was an amateur collector of these beautiful things. She believed that interest in the art and culture of other peoples adds richness to one's own life, furnishes the soil out of which springs that inspiration which must be passed on to teachers and children if the aims of education are to be attained.

The boys and girls whose poverty keeps them out of school are often even more appealing than the children whose maladjustments make it impossible for them to avail themselves of the opportunity that the city and good will offer. From the first acquaintance with our neighborhood, our emotions and thoughts were deeply stirred by the plight of the children who could not, because of the family need for their earnings, continue their schooling. We saved the dignity of the child by offering relief in the form of a scholarship, which was paid at regular intervals. At the same time we fixed in the mind of the parent (usually a widow) and of the child the idea that the scholarship was allotted him to make possible further and essential education, and that it gave the donors the right to know the uses the scholar was making of it. The purposes of such aid were sustained, and conferences with parent and teacher added to its importance. A friend provided the scholarship funds for individual children.

As the Settlement grew, its acquaintance with children multiplied. The awarding and supervision of scholarships were no longer for the individual, but were organized under a Scholarship Committee generously financed by club leaders. During the War, the Scholarship Committee functioned with the Red Cross, the latter endorsing the policy of keeping in school the children of men in service. Both the Scholarship Committee and the Vocational Guidance Bureau of the Settlement were under the same chairman, and, with a Junior Employment Service, in 1920 all were merged into the present admirable Vocational Service for Juniors.

Many of the educational features of these and other Settlement ventures, some of which anticipated the experimental schools, were due to the fresh approach and the inspiration of a young woman, then Rita Wallach.[3] With her trained mind and an unusual insight into educational needs, she inspired a devoted band of young people who, with her, initiated and carried out successful projects. From that leadership was developed — in addition to the Scholarship and Vocational Guidance enterprises — an admirable club technique. A training course for club leaders was a logical consequence.

[3] Rita Wallach Morgenthau.

Throughout this progress, the direct approach to the child, measures to ascertain the natural aptitudes, and the type of preparation and employment that would best accord with these aptitudes, were the primary consideration. A directory of vocational opportunities within the public schools and through private agencies was issued and revised from time to time. Under the enlarged and formulated scheme, the scholarships were usually provided for a two-year period of vocational training. The award was based on knowledge of home environment, personal characteristics, and school standing. Studies were made of wage-earning possibilities for children and other related interests. There were intermediate steps which should be recorded, indicating the methods employed by settlements and their associates, so that, when a demonstration period was over, their affiliations with responsible agencies committed to the same objective should be effected.

Henry Street's Scholarship Committee found ready coöperation in the public school, and first established its Vocational Guidance Bureau in Public School Number 147 on Henry Street. In 1916, in line with the same major interest, the Settlement financed the investigation made by the Mayor's Committee on Vocational Help to Minors. By 1919 their service was available through public schools in the several sections of the city. The Board of Education provided more office space in the school buildings, and various agencies, notably those offering supervised placement for juniors, coöperated in the undertaking. The public schools of New York City, with understanding of the needs

A Leader of the Unemployed

of the children, established the Department of Guidance, inspired by the demonstration of the Vocational Service for Juniors. A significant development that ensued was the provision for juvenile placement in the New York State Labor Department, the first legislation of this kind in the United States. At the Child Labor Conference in Washington a year ago, New York reported a State Juvenile Placement Service with ten offices, almost all in public school buildings, and a trained personnel, exclusive of clerical force, of sixteen members. So rewarding has been the experience with a specialized employment division for minors in New York's State Labor Department that we are convinced this provision for young wage earners is pledged to permanency.

And with the recognition that adequate vocational service for youth must be kept distinct from an adult employment service comes the need for trained and experienced counselors, ranking with high school teachers in specialized preparation. There is also widespread realization that some scheme of scholarship aid is essential to well-rounded vocational guidance.

From the first the conviction has prevailed that the service for juniors comprises three essential features — guidance, placement, and scholarships — if young people are to be successfully adjusted to their world. The Settlement continues to utilize this acceptable method for giving help to individuals (and it does not limit its aid to elementary school children) in accordance with the money available for such purposes. The chairman of the Scholarship Committee of the Vocational Service for Juniors, who also contributes her service as counselor, gives intelligent and sympathetic understanding of the problems of young wage earners.

Large-scale unemployment and the shortening of the work day and the work week have focused attention on a problem that has engrossed the settlements almost from their beginning: the development of cultural recreation and the happy, creative use of unoccupied time. To-day we realize that the matter of play challenges the best powers of educators and community leaders, for the needs are diverse and almost endless. While recreational opportunities cannot be left to haphazard good will, too much organization may defeat its own purpose. There is, after all, a place for profitable indolence; it would be a deadly thing to have all one's time scheduled. But, so far, overorganized Soviet Russia has on the whole provided better for its people's recreation of body and spirit through sports and play facilities than has any other government.

As part of our attempt to give youth a more adequate preparation for adult experience, we need to formulate a technique for instructing children in matters of sex. When we first went to Henry Street, the question had not been generally discussed. No books had been written for the laity. Later, when we were searching for guidance, we found a small volume written by Patrick Geddes.[4] When the great philosopher, educator, and town planner became our friend, I asked him what had diverted his attention to that subject. Said the man who did not believe in specialization, but

[4] Later Sir Patrick Geddes.

who was himself a specialist in many fields, "There was no literature; we could not educate the young in our Edinburgh school without intelligently facing this problem, but we found nothing, so I was obliged to write a book about it."

I am tempted to digress here, to tell another story about this man who was a light bringer to those who knew him. My country home is beautified by a small pool of fresh water. On acquiring the property we wanted to know the character of life in the pond, and I invited a biologist from a famous university to examine the water. He made his enthusiastic report, and added with congratulations, "You will never have mosquitoes there because the balance of insect life will protect you." Too unlearned in biology to ask what that "balance" was, I accepted the term and repeated it to others with a sense of satisfaction. Patrick Geddes, riding up the entrance road, cast one glance at the pond and said, "You are fortunate that your pond has so many dragon flies. The large ones will eat the mosquitoes, the young will eat the larvæ." He greatly simplified the "balance of insect life" — a lesson to instructors, that!

But to return to the subject of enlightening children on the most important subject of sex — we tried to persuade parents to talk with their girls and boys. We never found one among our neighbors who would do so, and we concluded that the lack of a vocabulary was a serious impediment. Given simple instruction, we felt sure the mothers could direct the lesson, and we urged that the fathers should share the responsibility.

We invited teachers of near-by schools to meet at the Settlement one afternoon a week for elementary instruction in sex hygiene and methods of presenting the information to young pupils, since at best many of the homes could not be relied upon to undertake the task. Miss Laura Garrett, author of one of the early books on the teaching of sex hygiene, was engaged to conduct the class. She urged that the instruction be kept out of the hands of those who would stress the danger of disease. Such instruction, she agreed with us, should rather glorify the sanctity of the human body and the responsibility of young people to themselves and to their future parenthood.

In addition to the lack of vocabulary, parents on our streets and in neighborhoods similar to ours are handicapped by a lack of privacy that it is hard for the better-housed family to comprehend. In a crowded tenement home, there is literally no opportunity for the well-intentioned father or mother to secure the sense of being alone and safe against interruption, so necessary to the discussion of this or other serious matters.

The professional educators could make no contribution to current life more useful than a revaluation of college experience and college degrees. America seems to be obsessed by the urge to send its youth to college, regardless of scholarly ambition or ability. In thirty-five years the enrollment has grown from 45,000 to over 500,000. An increasing number of college authorities bewail the wasted time of many of those who throng the campuses. One reason for mounting enrollments is undoubtedly the fact that a degree, in the boom years, became a commercial asset in business and industry as well as in the professional fields. Even the department store salesman was expected to have a college diploma. Among aspirants for the highest degrees, one frequently encounters a narrowness of outlook and lack of information that amount to ignorance in an educated person's sense. If true scholars are wholly engrossed in their own subject, their concentration cannot be criticized. But surely the distinction is clear between such devotion and the superficial learning of the student whose thinking is in terms of credits and a degree.

I have often been disheartened, particularly since the War, by the lack of interest in the universities (I speak of the great Eastern universities, with which I am more familiar) in the problems and the possibilities of the changing world. Perhaps this absence of ferment is due to the numbers of students who go to college for social reasons, or because "you need a degree to get on," or for lack of "something better to do." Perhaps it is symbolic of youth's belief that all is well in this best of worlds. Perhaps it reflects the numbing effects of mass education in childhood. I have repeatedly been told on authority that, with the exception of small, distinct groups, there is no apparent curiosity in student minds, none expressed through the student body. There is occasional yeasty discussion of the ethics of sport, of modern art and drama, of the present-day importance of the classics; but conformity and unquestioning respect for the *status quo* are said, in general, to prevail.

One can note a few outstanding exceptions. Trade-unionism, Soviet Russia, Sacco and Vanzetti, the Scottsboro case, Mooney's incarceration, have been discussed here and there, and some vigorous protests made. On the other hand, outspoken instructors have been disciplined by college administrators or boards of trustees. In New York City, a student editor was expelled shortly before graduation because he had aggressively criticized the college athletic association and the management of the student dining hall. Clearly, "unrest" in student or faculty circles may have uncomfortable consequences.

It is pleasing to note that among the colleges that do stand out for free expression women's colleges are usually mentioned; a group of coeducational colleges that includes the University of Chicago, the University of Wisconsin, Oberlin, Swarthmore, and others, ranks with them.   I am sorry that the men's colleges have not shown themselves more in accord with the fundamentals upon which this government is based: right of assemblage, freedom of expression, and respect for minority opinion.   It would be tremendously exhilarating to find forward movements, if not initiated, at least supported by the student body.   There may be something inherent in our protective attitude toward the young that helps explain their delayed participation in social and economic changes from which institutions of learning should not remain aloof.   This is not a new consideration.   Years ago many New Yorkers were troubled if not shocked by the action of students in a New York university who took the place of organized workers during a subway strike.

I once accepted an invitation to lecture before Phi Beta Kappa at Yale, though speech making is not my favorite occupation. I felt, however, that I had no right to refuse to draw attention to these evidences of indifference to — perhaps ignorance of — the importance of the laboring men's effort to better their conditions and to publicize their grievances. I told the young men that I doubted whether this alignment of students with capital against labor would then have been found in any other country in the world. To illustrate the absurdity of prejudices — economic, religious, racial — I told a story that we relished greatly at the Settlement.

My secretary reported to me that a friend I shall call "Mrs. Curry" had hurried to the House to tell us that her hard-working neighbor, Mrs. Flynn, could not go to her job that morning because her shoes would not hold together. I was glad to send the needed $2.50 to Mrs. Curry that she might without delay supply her neighbor's need, and because I knew it would please her to buy the shoes for Mrs. Flynn. It made a great impression. She moved her chair confidentially close to the secretary and said: "Ain't it grand! I'll tell you what, the day will come, I'm sure, whin we Protestants and Catholics will forgit our bigotries and come together to wipe the Jews off the face of the earth!"

However I may have failed to impress the Phi Beta Kappas with my grievance against students, the story itself must have gone over. Recently a member of that audience who has attained lofty position in an English university wrote to me that in his first lecture to the transatlantic class he repeated the message I tried to give and illustrated it with the story of Mrs. Curry.

Before my interest in this world has ended, I should like to know that our great educational institutions bring their students to grips with the question of what use they are to make of their training. It seems to me that the colleges and universities have failed in their purpose unless they have made the students face their obligations in vital living, in the relationships of men and women, in being ready for action as good citizens when the call for action comes.

In the House on Henry Street, as I suggested earlier in this chapter, education is not thought of as being confined within the classroom walls of schools or colleges. But even the informal educational experience of Settlement clubs and parties may be repelled if it is not offered with a regard for the susceptibilities of the uneducated. Though the fact has been stated again and again, in many ways and by many writers, it is difficult to comprehend how superficial are the differences between one person and another. Beneath the outer shell, marked with the disparities that are naturally striking on first acquaintance, one finds in any neighborhood just people — fine and coarse, happy and unhappy, dull and creative, in about the same proportion. To make the recent comer to our land feel more sympathetic to new overtures is merely to draw attention to the fact that the American way is not necessarily the superior way, that all lovers of humanity treasure character and the moralities, that there is endless variety in the formulation of beliefs. The realization of a common appreciation of beauty is important to this better understanding, and unlimited are the opportunities for its expression. It is often touching to realize how helpless in their selection are people with little money and without a background that defines beauty.

One of our club girls brought to the House a really atrocious hat, representing no small item in her budget. Her beloved club leader also had a new hat, and both were displayed. Said the owner of the atrocity, "I could not buy a hat like yours in the stores we go to; ours are all trimmed." How better could she state her appreciation? She realized that form and line constitute true art, but to her they seemed unattainable.

And once, when we had finished decorating the dance hall, a young man of the neighborhood expressed his pleasure in the effect. The scheme was simple, and I had doubted whether it would seem sufficient. The young man said, "Oh, I like it well enough. I like it very well. Those reds and greens and papers and mirrors and trimmings in the halls we rent — that 's what people think we like. You know, we have n't any choice."

We often are disheartened by the effect on our girls of rich women who, the girls think, "know everything" because they have the money to acquire "everything," and yet who display vulgar taste. Once, as a test of the instinct for beauty among a group of our girls, we selected an extreme and very unattractive mode of hairdressing then in style. We took up the subject by finding what women, among those pictured in the Sunday papers, were most admired. The majority voted for the photograph of Ethel Barrymore among the actresses, and a portrait painting of Mrs. Willard Straight, now Mrs. Leonard Elmhirst, which were reproduced in the rotogravure section. Neither had adopted the exaggerated mode, and much was made of their discrimination.

An appreciation of the beauty of great and unselfish living has been one of the most potent educational forces in every age. Thinking that the lads of our neighborhood were not likely to hear of the achievements of Americans, I suggested that we discuss at every meeting of our first boys' club the story of some American hero. We defined a hero as one who through his life had contributed to the betterment of America. That opened up a wide selection of artists, writers, pioneers, civil servants, scientists, Presidents. And though we pedaled softly on generals and war heroes, we did consider the heroism of military men who lived in periods when to be a soldier was the best way known of serving the country. We gave an honored place to Colonel Waring, who cleaned the streets, and to Josephine Shaw Lowell, who to a large extent first replaced sentimental and ephemeral philanthropy with the intelligent rehabilitation of those in need. We varied the programme with debates on the relative contributions of our heroes. There was one very heated discussion of the comparative courage of the settlers who came over in the *Mayflower* and Daniel Boone. The argument ran something like this:

"The Pilgrims believed in God and were sure they would land and be saved. But Daniel Boone was not that kind of a fellow and he went into the wilderness just the same." When we had, according to the president of the club, "run out of American heroes," we studied civics. Every reform movement believed to be unselfish and for the good of the people was strongly defended by members of the club who served in the campaign as soap-box orators, distributors of campaign literature, and the supporters of Seth Low, John Purroy Mitchel, "Teddy," and so on. Not a single member of that club is now an indifferent citizen.

It would be all too easy to write an entire chapter about Henry Street clubs. No two of them are alike in the circumstances of organization, the way they hold their meetings, their "rules," their programmes, their goals. And yet each one, almost always consciously, has functioned as a means of education, and as a source of mental and spiritual enrichment as well as of "good times." The "good times" are never lost to sight. The programmes of the very earliest clubs always left time for fun. The fun might be a sleigh ride (there have been miracles, and one treasured night of deep snow on the East Side when we improvised a sleigh and jingled off to Coney Island) or the theatre, or a hike with baseball at the end of it, or just a "party." We never consider a programme complete unless a third of the meeting is turned over to active play. A group may come into the House quite accidentally. One of the most successful organizations (and it has endured almost all the years of the Settlement's existence) followed an extremely unpleasant encounter with boys who were suspicious of strangers — and the way to register your suspicion is to be actively, aggressively opposed. Pioneers act, perhaps daringly, upon intuition and right feeling, and with purpose of helpful friendship. Plans and programmes inevitably follow.

A constitution for a boys' club, or for any club, holds in embryo the rights of the members, the obligation of support, the loyalty to an ideal. A group seldom rises above the stature of the leader, but an intelligent leader, unhampered by rules and routine, can bring the members to original thought and initiative. A more or less uncontrolled set of girls or boys is likely to imitate the neat dress and refinement of a person who never "preaches" and who not only provides unexpected pleasure but can introduce flavor even into "school stuff." Shabby rooms, we hold, are never economical when measured by results. Meticulous cleanliness, flowers, good pictures, we deem essential in the meeting places of these experimental social groups.

Some of the problems encountered in club organization help us understand both background and environment. One day when a group of a dozen boys had assembled to get acquainted with the leader proposed for them, we pointed out to the lads that the meetings would be held hereafter in the evenings, and we felt that their parents should know where they were going and with whom they would be associated on "club night." A call upon each household was indicated. Said one little lad, poorly dressed and with a suspicious bump on his forehead, "Don't you come to our house, Miss

Wald. They are awful fresh there and they don't care a damn where I go." Again there are, of course, the more intellectual parents, who investigate whether within the House there is freedom from propaganda, religious or otherwise, and whether we are likely to make membership "worth while."

In the freedom of settlement relationship, it is not difficult to recognize good impulses, and good impulses, if not dissolved by inaction, are the elements of character building. That kind of education replaces, though it does not necessarily eliminate, the more popular desire for efficiency. Efficiency, perhaps, is a pedal that has been pressed too hard.

One group that met as small boys over thirty years ago have demonstrated their friendship and loyalty and their participation in the promotion of the measures we hold important. The children of the original members are linked by ties of affection and common interest. Here is to the second generation evidence of the worth of the clubs.

For children from congested city areas to spend a summer fortnight in the country is in itself an educational experience, and at the farm and the camps conducted by the Settlement the education is at no cost to the fun. Dr. John Lovejoy Elliott, distinguished educator, Felix Adler's successor as leader of the Ethical Culture movement, and Head Worker of the Hudson Guild, says of our "country clubs": —

"After visiting the camps, I think that I have until now very much underestimated the possibilities of these summer colonies. I am not sure but that in such camps

the children get the very best possible help in learning
what a community spirit is, perhaps better than they
do at any other time during the year."

Many people who know the freedom and the standards
of the camps would agree with Dr. Elliott in seeing in
them great helpfulness to youth.   This seems to be the
appraisal of the girls and boys themselves, many of
whom, grown to maturity, cherish the memory of the
happy days in the country, year after year.   Perhaps
such results are obtained because the guests have an
orderly, joyous time, their days and nights uncompli-
cated by grown-up problems and demands.

At both farm and camp, buildings and equipment
have been given by men and women who in their
youth had enjoyed the beauty of these places.   It would
be impossible, in a few paragraphs, to convey a rounded
picture of this country experience and all it means —
the songs that have been written, the ideals accepted,
the more serious memories intertwined with the recol-
lections of loveliness and gayety.   It is not strange that,
separated from city life, the children should for a time
forget its sordid aspects.   Their comments upon their
new experiences are often as delightful as they are
startling.

During one terrible hailstorm, a small girl expressed
her disapproval of the visitation: "God's getting awful
fresh, throwing down those big stones!   First thing He
knows, He'll hit somebody."   Whereupon a little
comrade poked her vigorously and exclaimed, "Becky,
you must n't talk like that about God!   Most everybody on our block likes Him."

Such enjoyment of the holidays presents a great contrast to the early days, when going to the country was an unknown and somewhat intimidating experience. To-day there is great faith in the recuperative powers of "fresh air," as the two weeks' outing is usually called, and the beauty of the hills and fields, the trees and flowers, of the sunset over the lake, of birds and butterfly wings, is measured and appreciated.

But though we on Henry Street count these out-of-school influences as education, we do not belittle the wisdom and the inspiration that are found in books. Personally, I view with regret the diminishing library of fairy tales and folklore. In a mechanical age, it is exciting to see a child work on airplane models and identify the make of automobiles from a distance, but not at too great a price of literal-mindedness and stunted imagination. I was reading a tale to a little boy not quite six, and I pointed to an illustration of an overcast sky. The story dealt with the journey of a horse and its owners to a fair. Indicating the cloud, I said, "I am afraid they will have rain." Said the small boy, "Excuse me, I don't think that 's a cloud. I think it 's a dirigible."

Recent years have brought a saner recognition of what the truth means to children, and such deceptions as stories about the "stork" are not as general as once they were. But fairy tales, I believe, are an essential part of every child's education, and, for that matter, of every grown-up's sustenance. Naturally I take for granted a clear distinction between lovely and stirring fairy tales and unscientific statements given out as

truths. I am aware that in this realistic period the old
tales and fancies are taboo among some people. But
this seems to me as extreme as another generation's
careless mixing of truth and falsehood in talking with
children. I hope it will soon be modified, and that we
shall have back the stories that stimulate the imagination so wonderfully in their proper place and time.

It is heartening to realize how frankly one can deal
with a child. Two youngsters, almost babies, asked if
there was really a Santa Claus. When thus challenged
to tell the truth, I acknowledged that there is no old man
who goes down chimneys with a pack on his back, but
that there is a spirit of love of which people have tried to
make a picture by creating the story of Santa Claus.
So far as I know, they lost nothing of the Christmas
joy, of the tree and the stocking, the excitement and
the mystery of the day. I heard one of them explain
to a group of little friends, "Santa is a spirit and it's
just the same."

It would be easy to exceed the limits of this book with
stories that show the effect of indirect education, even
of education in what we call "the tool subjects," that
proceeds with regard to childish individuality rather
than a formal system. Intelligent parents as well as
teachers exercise ingenuity for the unusual child. One
dear little boy of five spoke learnedly of the fertilization
of butterflies and was excited by the wonders of the life
he found in the water. He knew birds and beasts and
all things that grew and flew, but he was completely
uninterested in reading or writing. He did not care
for pictures unless they portrayed his beloved creatures,

and his indifference to formal school subjects did not change as he grew older.   Then the inspiration came to one of his elders that he might be interested in keeping a catalogue of his treasures.   He eagerly fell in with the plan, but found at once that he needed to spell the names to carry out the project and write them down and number them.   And then his conventional education was started.

Not long ago I received a charming letter from a former member of one of the boys' clubs, who said, "I have been saving up to go to Europe.   I have enough to go third class.   I have been thinking of this ever since the picture postcards that you received were posted on the bulletin board and I thought to myself, 'Some day I am going to every one of those places.' "

Such chances to open new windows for children of meagre experience come to settlement people who are not hampered by rigid programmes and who have the privilege of rare intimacy with their neighbors.

The development of the arts at the House has been, I think, our most stirring and rewarding adventure in "indirect education."   Here is recreation in its truest sense, filling the vacuum of the unintelligent waste of time, the resourcelessness of the hours after school or work.

When we open the door of the House on Henry Street and see the steps crowded with youngsters returned from camp, singing so well the songs they have helped compose; when we listen to their reminiscences, eager as those of men returned from far travels, we are glad they are not shooting craps.   We treasure the "hymn" written by a youth who had no knowledge of music, who felt unnatural when he returned to the hot city streets after his two weeks in camp. He found himself humming an accompaniment to verses he had written, and asked if the sounds he felt were music. These "sounds" were taken down, and the song is often sung: —

MOTHER HENRY

All earth to-day your glory's proclaiming,
    For that you've stood beside us,
Holding the torch of righteousness flaming,
    Striving aright to guide us.

Chorus

Mother Henry, we'll remember you
    When other mem'ries fade;
Keeping the thought of the gladness you brought,
    And each sacrifice you made.
In childhood days you made life worth living,
    Youth's pathway you made brighter.
One creed: to serve! not asking, but giving.
    You've made our burdens lighter.

Hints of talent are watched, though our first concern is not with solo successes. But we are human, and we are glad that one of our own was acclaimed for his characterization in the play, *Grand Hotel*, which the critics singled out for special praise. Neither are we too modest to refer to distinguished painters whose work the French Government purchased. We urge every new recruit to the Settlement to be on the lookout for indications of special interest, anything that will serve as a clue to helpfulness. Our most discouraging "bad boy" at last displayed one small talent — the way he played the mouth organ for the clog dancers on the street or in the gym. His sense of rhythm was so good it finally made a place for him in a not too fastidious brass band.

Floyd Anderson, the janitor, and for many years a support and comfort to the staff, encouraged a new resident who was troubled about the noisy, obstreperous boys: "Don't worry, Miss. I've been here so long — I've often seen them come in wild and go out gentlemen."

Again and again it is borne in upon me that people who think seriously are likely to place play and joy and beauty among the essentials for a successful civilization, despite our Puritan heritage of those who "willfully lived in sadness." The stern qualities that make for stern character are not inevitably separated from the more colorful demands of the spirit. Our experience on Henry Street shows that outlets through the arts and crafts — music, painting, pottery, woodwork, and kindred projects — give more lasting satisfaction when they are shaped by teachers who, in their approach to both child and grown-up, recognize the high educational significance of these activities.

Our pottery shop was organized by a talented teacher who is now the director of the art department in the Settlement. From it there went to the Century of Progress Exposition a beautifully modeled representation of the back of the House on Henry Street, and the garden which was converted into the first organized public playground in New York. There are tiny figurines of nurses and residents in the costumes of the nineties, and the children are conscientiously observing the one rule of the yard: that the girls who used the "scups" (swings) must wear panties or diapers. The Settlement has found, as have so many potters, that, to children struggling to find an expression for creative instincts, clay is usually the best medium.

Under the direction of a gifted woman, the music school now holds a distinguished place in our programme. It was established after many years of music in classes, in clubs, in orchestra, in balalaika ensemble, in glee clubs. Important place has of recent years been given to the more informal social music, which lends renewed life to old folk songs and melodies.

But none of our activities in the arts is to be compared with the contributions made by Alice and Irene Lewisohn through their inspired leadership in the festivals, in music, the dance, and the many arts of the theatre. Their achievement displays never a moral, but always a purpose. They first came to Henry Street as young girls, and they brought with them rare gifts of personality and talent. They served a long apprenticeship with clubs and classes, but soon began to originate art forms through new combinations of the elements of the drama and of pageantry. They added a house to the Settlement group, so that the gym might be enlarged to accommodate a movable stage. They were the guiding spirits in an outdoor theatre on the farm, and provided entertainment for the near-by village. Later, their vision and experience brought about the building of the Neighborhood Playhouse.

Now that the activities of the Neighborhood Playhouse have stepped from a local to a wider field, where they function as a separate organization, it is interesting to look back over the steady growth from informal club activities to a professional theatre and a school recognized for high artistry.

In the early experiments in the clubs, these young women found the first germs of the beautiful festivals. The club programmes included stories from the Eastern epics and from the myths of Greece, with pantomimic interpretation of the timeless tales. The close of the season brought together a lyrical expression: "The Three Impressions of Spring." Each spring was welcomed with a festival which conveyed through folk tradition the idea of rebirth or resurrection which, in some form, is common to all peoples and all creeds. Though comparatively crude, these celebrations in movement, song, and color were the basis of the widely praised Henry Street Festivals. When more sustained training was required than was possible in club periods, special classes in dancing, pantomime, and choral singing were organized, and increased opportunity was given to obtain practice in scenery, property, and costume making. When all this activity encroached too far on the Settlement House, the Neighborhood Playhouse was built. It became the setting of the festivals and the plays, and throughout its growth carried on its first forms of expression: lyric and dramatic productions. The Festival Dancers and the Neighborhood

IN THE WINGS OF THE PLAYHOUSE

Players worked side by side, sometimes combining their programmes, sometimes alternating. Various experiments were tried.

At one period, selected motion pictures with interludes of music, dances, or one-act plays were offered. This ceased when a ruling by the Picture Managers Board prohibited the selection of films by exhibitors, and left no choice but the acceptance of the regular commercial service.

One must regret that the potentialities of the movies have not been exploited for the benefit of the vast audiences they draw. They might so easily have become an unqualified influence for good, and they are so often a definite influence for evil. Their provisions for entertainment have become Gargantuan in importance and effect. It is hopeless to try to modify or control them by small, individual effort.

The Neighborhood Playhouse next gave place to the fundamental conceptions of creative theatre production. The Misses Lewisohn found it necessary to concentrate on plays, acting, and the means of production to a degree not possible with an organization exclusively amateur. Though spirited and intelligent, with a standard hard to match on Broadway, the majority of the Neighborhood Players had neither the maturity nor the qualifications for sustaining major rôles in such plays as clamored for production — for instance, *The Mob*, by John Galsworthy. The universality of its theme, the poignancy of its appeal in the period of war hysteria, as well as its qualities as a play, made it as suitable a link between the old and the new phases of the Playhouse as had been *Jephthah's Daughter*, which, years earlier, had emphasized a departure in technique and proportion, while retaining the spirit of the earlier festivals in the gym. For this expanded plan it was necessary to give a nightly instead of a week-end performance, and the full-time professional actor, with his specialized training and experience, seemed an indispensable factor of the new programme. But the professional alone, it was thought, could not express the Neighborhood Playhouse idea; the amateur, too, was essential. Both had a part in the new development.  This was evidenced by the fact that the title rôle of *The Mob* was played by amateurs.

Years of working together had established a point of view among the amateurs. When it was decided to organize a permanent company, the attempt to recruit players from among available Broadway actors proved that, without special training and a period of adjustment, the creative approach to production, according to the Neighborhood Playhouse ideal, was not possible. The repertory plan, in its final form, grew out of many mechanical problems. It was launched in order to meet the expediency of a situation that swung the Neighborhood Playhouse more and more into the complexity of organization necessary for the running of a theatre. When the structure and scheme as it existed at 566 Grand Street impeded a freer development of the idea,— that is, when it was realized that the pressure of the expedient would gradually compel a departure from the more informal point of view,— the closing of the Neighborhood Playhouse was inevitable.

The dramatic work of the Settlement has returned to its original purpose. Its department is under the direction of a gifted and trained leader who finds inspiration in the neighborhood and its people, and gives to them enthusiasm for their work with her. Carefully selected plays, with settings and costumes made by the amateurs, draw interested audiences. Instruction in diction and speech rivals in interest the dancing lessons, and to these classes come older people who have learned to appreciate the importance of well-spoken English in their different jobs, professional and office. The Little Theatre brings lovers of music to the chamber music concerts provided by the Settlement Music School. The Gordon, the Musical Arts, the Stradivarius Quartettes, and others of equal quality, testify to their reward in the obvious pleasure and appreciation of the audience. And the Little Theatre also furnishes a place for large and less personal meetings, when questions of the day are discussed by experts. At these meetings the different political parties have the privilege of expounding their platforms and putting forward their candidates.

The Neighborhood Playhouse, no longer on Grand Street, carries on a more diversified programme in an-

other location. But its gifts, offered from the little
Grand Street theatre, are treasured memories. The
demonstration made by the Misses Lewisohn constitutes
a rare contribution to the history of the American
theatre; their unyielding standards of good taste and
technique will not be forgotten. The distinguished
associates who took part are almost too numerous to be
cited. There was Sarah Cowell Lemoyne, an interpreter
— perhaps our best interpreter — of Browning, and
prized long after Browning faddists had taken up other
devotions. Yvette Guilbert (translated by the tiniest
class members as "Yetta Gilbert") taught and took
part with enthusiasm in the mediæval French miracle
play, *Gibour*. But I think I loved best Walt Whitman's *Salut au Monde*. So exciting was this performance that distinguished people asked for the
privilege of having a place in the processional that ended
the play; the enthusiasm reached the colored porter,
magnificent in form, who asked to march as the representative of his race, with naked thorax. The first
presentation was a simple one to reëncourage me on
my return from abroad in 1919. Whitman's conception of democracy was a good antidote to the after-
War pessimism felt throughout Europe. Later *Salut*
was expanded into a beautiful performance.

The Neighborhood Playhouse Studios on Madison
Avenue conduct classes for young men and women who
wish to enter some branch of theatrical work, and "who
seek a training in the technique of the various arts of
this composite profession." The staff includes distinguished artists who unite in the ideal of directing the

creative programme. The work for the Juniors, started so many years ago in association with the Settlement, draws old and new groups to these studios, under the same inspiring leadership which characterized the first Henry Street efforts. In addition to these offerings, Miss Irene Lewisohn projects a once-a-year production at an opera house or other auditorium ample enough to accommodate a full orchestra. The first to illustrate her purpose was the presentation of Bloch's symphony, "Israël," at the Manhattan Opera House, with the Cleveland Symphony Orchestra, led by Nikolai Sokoloff, and a company of talented actors and dancers.

A learned Hindu scholar, after seeing the Grand Street production of *The Little Clay Cart*, wrote: "It is quite fortunate that our *Mricchakatika*, the fifth-century Hindu play by King Sudraka, has first been produced in New York at the Neighborhood Playhouse, a theatre where, according to John Galsworthy, 'Magic has come to stay.'" That production and *The Dybbuk* will remain the outstanding exhibitions of what could be accomplished by selfless enthusiasts with a genius for hard work, by their associates, and by a sympathetic audience that gave atmosphere and splendid appreciation. The *Nation* listed the two Lewisohn sisters in its 1924 Roll of Honor, "For *The Dybbuk*, part of the beautiful experiment of the Neighborhood Playhouse in 'pure theatre.'" Joseph Wood Krutch called their work "unique in the history of the theatre."

The *New York Times* critic commented when the theatre closed: "The outgrowth of a 'social settlement' on the East Side of New York, almost the furthest East

A Pupil in the Music School

Side, had become a force of which the whole country was aware. From the beginning it had been working toward coördinating all the dramatic contributory arts into a harmonious whole."

Through the informal workshops and the studios, through recreation as well as through the beautiful festivals and the plays, through music and the opportunities that have presented themselves, intertwining education and the arts, it is impressed upon us that the world has barely awakened to the force and the importance that may be afforded to old and young, to the happy, to the weary, and to the inhibited. The writer has designedly emphasized the arts, the influence of creative expression and the sense of new powers, as an essential part of education. G.B.S., our modern stimulator, has felt the urge of this: "Every device of art should be brought to bear on the young, so that they may discover some form of it that delights them naturally, for there will come to all of them that period between dawning adolescence and full maturity when the pleasures and emotions of art will have to satisfy cravings which, if starved or insulted, may become morbid and disgraceful satisfactions, and, if prematurely gratified otherwise than poetically, may destroy the stamina of the race." [5]

But long, long ago Confucius, out of his wisdom, spoke thus: "Man has no place in society unless he understands æsthetics."

[5] *Bernard Shaw*, by Frank Harris.

VIII

THE CHILD AND THE LAW

Law is a human institution. All legal systems are man-made, and none of them are static. They express the changing attitude of human beings toward one another, and from year to year they register, particularly where the child is concerned, changes in opinion. Even the words in which laws are written may indicate the convictions of the time.

At different periods in the life of our Republic, the child has been the focus of effort toward social progress, though unfortunately our good purpose has not always been translated into effective action. America has, however, developed far-reaching safeguards for its youth and is, to many foreigners, a field for profitable observation and training. But much has not been covered, and it is worth while to analyze briefly how far we have gone.

At first, English practices were transplanted to the colonies, and in most states the Common Law, embodying the customs of seventeenth-century England, still prevails where it has not been superseded by statutory law.

Colonial records show the beginning of community responsibility for child welfare in attempts to make education compulsory. The first law to this end, passed in Massachusetts in 1642, marked a real advance over similar English legislation of the period. But the effort was short-lived, and it was not until the early years of the nineteenth century that universal education, as necessary for the existence of democracy, was seriously discussed. Perhaps the first uneasiness over child wage earners in this country was expressed in 1824, when a group of Massachusetts citizens demanded legislative investigation of conditions surrounding working children. At the time of the Civil War (1860) only six states had passed school attendance laws.[1]

Minimum-age regulations for factories were explicit; but how low were the limits set! Children six years of age were "exempted from school if lawfully employed," and the most advanced protection of the children — and this only in one state — prohibited factory work for those under twelve. The hours were usually from sunrise to sunset.

After the Civil War, labor statistics were gathered in some states, and revealed that children as young as seven were working long hours in industry. At that time,

[1] Massachusetts, Connecticut, Rhode Island, Maine, New Hampshire, Pennsylvania.

almost in the language of the modern social worker, was expressed this growing public opinion: "Human progress can only be realized when the new generation surpasses the previous."

To-day, the law is invoked to help remedy innumerable conditions of exploitation, of ignorance, of cruelty; its strong arm ranges from punishment for abandonment, brutality, desertion and neglect, to accident compensation, public education, health protection, and pensions for widows enabling children to remain in the environment best suited to their development. The progressive steps are many, the details sometimes confusing, but the subject should be studied by those readers who seek to understand social evolution in the modern world.

The dependence on law for the ultimate protection of children is tremendously significant, for it reflects a growing consciousness of child welfare as basically important to the common good. State interference between the family and the child springs from the realization that the future well-being of society depends upon the health, education, and sound principles of the oncoming generation and that these are not private family matters. Naturally the underprivileged children — those who suffer from orphanage, neglect, poverty, and exploitation in its many forms, or from their own delinquency or abnormality — greatly outnumber the more fortunate. They call for public protection as well as for public sympathy. They must be set in the way to the good life by those who have power and wisdom to see in the neglect of the child a danger to the country.

Looking back, one realizes almost with a shock how few are the years since parents carried the sole responsibility for the child, how short is the time since the first steps were taken to protect the child from the incompetent, cruel, or greedy parent. The Society for the Prevention of Cruelty to Children, formed in New York to rescue children from obvious physical abuse, resulted from the historic case of little "Mary Ellen." That was in 1875, and was, ironically, an outgrowth of the organized effort to prevent cruelty to animals, started nine years earlier.[2] Similar societies were soon active in other parts of the country. Largely as the result of their efforts, laws against abandonment of children, begging and peddling, child exploitation in circus and acrobatic acts, participation in dangerous occupations, or in work injurious to morals, life, or limb, have gradually been written into the statutes. In some states there have been added provisions to protect children from indecent liberties by adults and to prevent the sale of liquor, cigarettes, and drugs to minors.

There have been occasions when, in despair, an S O S went out to the local S.P.C.C. from Henry Street. Thus our nursing service was once notified by neighbors of the need of a sick child, obviously in exceeding pain.

[2] The brutal mistreatment of "Mary Ellen" was discovered by a young woman visiting a New York tenement on a charitable errand. Seeking help for the child, the visitor was advised by police officials, by her lawyer, and by her pastor, not to "interfere between parent and child." She finally appealed to the Society for the Prevention of Cruelty to Animals, and through that agency the child was rescued. Soon after, the S.P.C.C. was formed, under the first statute in the world for the prevention of cruelty to children.

It proved to be a meningitis case.   The parents refused medical assistance.   They allowed a Henry Street nurse to come in, but only to "come in" — not even to place ice upon the child's head.   Having tried unsuccessfully every persuasive argument, we reported the situation to the S.P.C.C. as a case of cruelty, and they were able, with their physician's support, to remove the suffering child to the hospital.

In the differences between parents and children, often the obvious difficulty is the impatience on both sides. It is hard for parents, brought up in old traditions, to adjust themselves to modern points of view.   This persists from the long ages during which parents owned their children legally.   They had the power of life and death over them.   They could hire them out for prostitution or use them for begging, as is not unknown to-day in any city.   They could abandon them and indenture them.   It is sometimes difficult for mothers and particularly for fathers to realize that in this country to-day the State is the ultimate guardian, and it is a question whether the State should not more often be empowered to protect children from their parents.   In many homes of high as well as low economic status, children are surrounded by love but not by understanding.

Old-country traditions often bring these parent-child conflicts into the courts.   Italians are sometimes most perplexed by the situation here.   One Italian couple from our neighborhood took their boy to court as incorrigible.   The father appeared in the same court a month later, appealing for the return of his "incorrigible" son.

Said the judge, "Have you changed your mind in this short time?"

"No," said the father, "me no change my mind — my wife she change my mind." And he added, referring to a recent suffrage parade: "America different. Did you see those ladies walk?"

In nothing pertaining to children has there been greater change than in the popular attitude toward young delinquents. Quite apart from the desirable emphasis on child guidance, we have come to realize that juvenile wrongdoing does not always in and of itself produce adult criminality. Because a boy "takes," whether it be wood for fires or apples to eat, it does not follow that when he graduates into manhood he will pick pockets or rob banks. Breaking open the school supply cupboard does not presage a career of safebreaking. The average youngster will probably become a law-abiding citizen. Corrective measures are needed for the troublesome minority. Such agencies as the settlements, the juvenile courts, the Crime Prevention Bureau, the Gerry Society, and the George Junior Republic are designed for their improvement.

The advent of the juvenile court heartened the men and women who knew children and were convinced that delinquents should be helped, not punished, and that at no time in the life of the child is it more important to give him the benefit of individual thought and care than when he has strayed. The earliest juvenile courts were in Denver and Chicago. In New York, the first court for child offenders was held in 1902. Since that time, there has been steady growth in the idea and its application. In the beginning, children were arrested and sent to jail in the "Black Maria." There was no probation system, and parole officers were volunteers, pledged only to six weeks' service, and supplied by social agencies.

In the three decades after that first children's court in New York, the personnel has been increased to include a presiding justice with five associate justices and the needed assistants. A probation department has been developed, and, most important, a clinic with psychiatrists, psychologists, and the aids needed by these scientific students of the children. The most recent step was the amalgamation of the Court of Domestic Relations with the Children's Court, which took place on October 1, 1933. Here the law has again recognized the unity of the family, and the need to know, in this field as in the sciences, the underlying causes of observed behavior, whether of atoms or of girls and boys. It is not unimportant to remind the reader that much can be saved in childhood and in happiness, as well as in taxpayers' money, by the early recognition of antisocial tendencies.

Judge Jonah J. Goldstein as magistrate has strongly stated his conviction that without the aid of social study a judge is helpless to deal with the great majority of offenders brought before him. Given a trained and adequate personnel, effective handling of young delinquents will clearly be facilitated by the new organization of the court dealing with problems of childhood and of family life. On the other hand, the best organization can be defeated in its purpose if entrusted to untrained and indifferent political appointees. That is the unfortunate experience of social workers in New York and other cities under "machine" control.

Judge Franklin C. Hoyt, presiding judge of the Children's Court, once told a story in the sitting room of the House on Henry Street which I repeat because it gives a picture of many elements that enter into the life of the boys that I know.[3]

Harry's mother sold fish in the market. The fish should have been covered, but were not. She was arrested for this violation of the sanitary code; and not having the two dollars to pay her fine, she was sentenced to the Tombs for twenty-four hours. Apparently her circumstances were not made clear to the presiding judge. He later stated that he did not know that her refusal to pay the fine was due to the fact that she had no money, nor that her small children were alone at home, frightened and hungry. But Harry found them in pitiable plight, and, searching for the absent mother, discovered her whereabouts. Harry was outraged by the wrong done to his mother and the cruelty to the children. He wrote an abusive letter to the judge — a pitiful letter, too, for this little David warned the Goliath of the court of the vengeance that would fall upon him. After pouring mounting insults upon the offending magistrate, he concluded: —

When I grow older, I am going to pronounce Humanity in the name of God, after I am avenged for my mother, and help this country to be free. Oh, if I only had the time I

[3] The story is related in detail in *Quicksands of Youth*, by Franklin Chase Hoyt (Scribner).

would tell you a whole lot more. But before I close I want to advise you to try to mend these circumstances. You won't live in luxury all the time. There is a God above who is running this earth and he is watching you patiently for committing such a crime as you have committed.

The judge to whom this letter was sent, greatly disturbed, forwarded it to the judge of the Children's Court, as the lad was too young to be brought before him. Judge Hoyt, wise and understanding, asked the boy to see him. There was nothing frightsome in the court room. The boy did not know it was a court. As man to man, the judge explained why fish had to be covered, how unfortunate it was that the judge who sentenced the mother did not have a social worker ready to inquire and make clear to him the circumstances; and then this friend of children tried to make Harry see that the letter he had written was not worthy of a thoughtful boy. A few days later, the "guilty" judge received another letter in which Harry asked for forgiveness, told a bit about the hungry household and how eager he was to go to school, and gave a touching clue to his state of mind by saying: —

You can have my friendship now and ever, and I also would like you to send me the name of the judge who took up my case for I must thank him more than anyone else for the good he has this day done to me. Enclosed I am sending you my best wishes and beloved friendship, and hoping that you will accept my apology with great amity, I am . . .

The tale ends happily, for the recipient of the letters, in dignified and kindly manner, apologized in turn to Harry, and all is well.

No one who hears the Children's Court stories can fail to react to the pity of the child and the rescue of the individual.   The evening the story of Harry was told, we also had as guests at Henry Street members of the party accompanying the King and Queen of Belgium, who were then visiting this country.   In spite of differences in background, they felt no less than we the implications of Harry's experience, and were obviously shocked at the extremes to be found in New York.

Henry Street's experience with youth in conflict with the law is usually a service both to court and to child. Provisions for protecting girls and boys through membership in Settlement clubs and classes, the country outings, the confidence of parents and guardians in the Settlement, are good preventives against antisocial behavior.   When we come into court it is almost always because judges, probation officers, and other law enforcement officials ask — and I believe always receive — help from the settlements in carrying out the socialized legislation that is in such contrast to the old idea of punishment.   Also the parents, particularly the mothers, turn to us for help.   Even when their own children are not involved they are concerned with neighborhood dangers to youth.   They themselves would not dare risk persecution by the police or retribution from the "fence" or other underworld agency involved, but come in secrecy to tell the trusted Settlement friends of the perils close to them. Through these sources we have been able to get rid of "fences" who accept stolen brass without question, as well as boxes of shirts and other goods, for which cash is paid.   At least three times within recent years we have been able thus to uncover hidden "dope." Now and again a mother will make us wise as to where the very young are gambling. Their effort, as ours, is to help the city and the community against what we know to be the despoiling of the child and his future.

Neighborhood and settlement influences are important factors in the lives of children. The contrast often causes the tenement child to imitate the best in the community rather than to follow inferior patterns close to him. All too often the child's misbehavior is due, not to precept or example, but to poverty itself — the inability of the parents to procure what they themselves recognize as the child's need. "Poverty is the curse of the poor!"

The rumor of a "bad" girl drew the Settlement to her. It was plain that the difficulties were due to "boarders," men without families living in the crowded home, and to the helplessness of the parents in handling the situation. The obvious thing to do was to take the girl from the neighborhood, where even the children called her offensive names. The father and mother had recognized that that was the course to follow, but the cost of moving far from old haunts was beyond them. The Henry Street friend accompanied the girl to court and told the whole story, agreeing to loan money for the moving expenses and to help the family find a desirable new location. The court readily concurred in this, and it has all worked perfectly. In a neighborhood that knows nothing of her "past" the little girl appears to be like any child. The father, after a hard day's labor, comes from a distant part of the Bronx to pay back in small sums the money that was advanced. This from an Italian, so near the line of pressing need, is the best possible proof of his appraisal of the help given.

The sex problem of adolescents in all its ramifications comes up frequently as the cause of delinquency and crime. It is a question so involved that its effective handling must rest with trained educators, social workers, and psychiatrists, not with punitive legislation.

A group of boys several years ago came reluctantly to report — though they hated to "snitch" — that they "felt I ought to know" that one of their number had fallen into the hands of a "vamp." Inquiring into the circumstances, I learned that the woman was a procuress, and that the boy had come under her influence at a public dance hall, and was used by her in her "trade." I went at once to our friend, the District Attorney of the period, and laid the facts before him. He telephoned a few days later to say that the woman had been sent out of the city to the community from which she came. There she was well known, and youth could be warned against her. The boy was in the District Attorney's office. What did I want done with him? "Send him down to the Settlement," was the suggestion. The boy came, in a rage against his friends who had "tattled" and against me. A long, long talk, far into the night, brought his experience into a truer perspective. How to handle the boy was not an easy matter. He ought not to be cut off from wholesome social contacts; but, on the other hand, he could not be permitted companionship with the young girls who came to our dances until we had some certainty that he was purged

ONE OF THE METAL WORKERS

of the disastrous influences.   Since he could not come
to the dances without a partner, the members of the
Settlement family were offered on the sacrificial altar.
But the poor boy hung around the dance rooms as if
the portals of Heaven were closed to him.   Later he was
restored to fellowship, and it is pleasant to recall that
the elder brother, the head of the family, was in absolute
accord with me on the main points of the programme —
suitable discipline, no nagging at home, testing of the
"reform" by school records and the judgment of the
boys who had uncovered the situation to me.   I may add
that the boy has gone through college and is, so far as
I know, serving acceptably in the executive position he
now holds.   Had it not been for the District Attorney,
who knew how to utilize the Settlement's help, the
young man would have been brought in time to arrest
and disgrace.   Keeping him from court was in the
District Attorney's judgment and in ours the best protection for him and for the community.

Incidentally, the attitude of the boy's friends, and his
reaction to their difficult decision, raises interesting questions of loyalty.   Here the primitive rules of "the
gang" might have defeated the higher responsibility
of a friend's welfare.   Is it not a subject that challenges
educators and social thinkers?   Too often primitive
conventions prevail over the greater loyalties that, if
recognized, would break down silence and give helpful
information.

Legal machinery cannot always function happily for
youth's protection.   In these days runaways often appear in court for stealing an auto or for petty pilfer-

ing. Obviously those who run away for adventure, to seek work, or to escape from anxious, depressed homes, but who commit no crime, ought not to be dealt with as delinquents.

On a bright Sunday morning, the paper told of two small boys who had been arrested as runaways and were held in the Tombs. They had been "picked up" in the freight yards, after having "bummed" their way from Dayton, Ohio, to New York. The picture of two little fellows, charged with no serious delinquency, locked in the notorious prison, gripped us. One of the residents went to the Tombs, armed with my offer of guardianship and pledge to send the lads home if, upon investigation, that seemed the way we should like to have our own little brothers treated. After miraculous cutting of red tape, back came the resident with two white-faced, scared eleven-year-olds. When questioned, they confessed that, inspired by Sunday newspaper pictures, they had left home to see Brooklyn Bridge and the Singer Building. A long-distance call to the Dayton Y.M.C.A. brought the information that they were the sons of skilled workmen, employed in an automobile plant. The railways granted reduced rates, and I invested in tickets for the lads. I had many pangs at sending them back to Dayton without showing them New York, but I feared they might be tempted to further running away. They were given maximum bathing and minimum pocket money and put on the train. The astonishing result was that the parents bore me no little ill-will because I had interfered with what they felt might have been a "big chance" for their sons.

They must have remembered the heroic legends of Horatio Alger, and expected their boys to win fame and fortune. Apparently they completely overlooked the perils of their frightened youngsters, including the night in jail. They expressed their disapproval of my course by omitting repayment of the money spent for the boys' return.

It is not easy to draw the line between social and antisocial behavior. Thus fighting, often so disturbing to adults, seems to be a normal part of boy life, and unless carried to extremes does not as a rule result disastrously to life, limb, or character. But street fights are always bigger fights in embryo, and at Henry Street we have many chances to see the amusing or pathetic sides of these boyish conflicts, as well as to forestall their more serious possibilities.

Called to the door one afternoon by an excited mob of Jewish boys who had been playing football (the ball provided by the Settlement), I learned that "the Cherry Street Micks" had "swung in." The burden of the children's frantic screams was, "Help us! The Christians have got the ball!"

On another occasion a boy dashed in, placed something moist in my hand, shouting, "Keep it for me — there 's a fight — " and rushed off, leaving me the surprised guardian of his glass eye.

But in court, all spontaneity and enthusiasm vanish. They are with rare exceptions frightened, sick youngsters. At Henry Street we do not let court experience serve as the social tie that brings children together. As far as is expedient, we scatter those with "records" among the wholesome, no more in one group than can be assimilated.

There are exceptions, of course, to any programme that deals with life. One summer night seven small boys entered "by force" a warehouse where it was known that ice cream was stored. To "swipe" ice cream does not seem a serious offense, but this was "forcible entry," and thereby became a felony. They were neighborhood boys and not bad — they just wanted ice cream. The judge knew by experience and sympathy that this was not a matter for the court but for the Settlement, and the culprits were turned over to us. They were engaging young things and terribly frightened, but they are all right now. It is pleasing to note that this summer, when newspaper stories had aroused interest in the theft of a treasured bench at the Settlement door, it was this group that secretly built a bench to replace the stolen one, and so became the admired heroes of the street. In dealing with the seven, we let "the pals," as they call themselves, "stick together," and it has worked!

There are no reliable figures to prove that there is truth in the perennial charge that juvenile delinquency is increasing, despite the facts of the wandering children, the temptations of the automobile, and the unhappiness in depressed homes.

While great gains have been made in the last two decades in understanding juvenile delinquency and in handling it, much remains to be done.

In classifying both adults and minors, the law proceeds solely on the basis of chronological age. Modern understanding of psychology and behavior is over-looked. A person twenty-one years of age but with the capacity of a child of six is an adult under the law — a great gap between our knowledge and its social application. At present, it is impossible to bring this type of offender into the children's court, which is so much better equipped to deal with him.

A most important practical help would be to have a police force trained as participants in the social process, and not merely as disciplinarians. Arthur Woods, former Commissioner of Police in New York City, had this goal in view. At the Settlement, we have often had intelligent coöperation from the police, and we know its value. One precinct captain, at our request, called in plain clothes to advise neighborhood families on protective measures for their "problem" boys, instead of appearing in uniform to arrest them. But such insight and tact are not usual.

Henry Street, not illogically, has been most deeply concerned with measures to protect the working child, and to regulate the conditions under which he labors.

The New York Child Labor Committee grew out of a subcommittee of the University Settlement, organized under the chairmanship of the Head Resident, Robert Hunter, in 1902. Two years later the National Child Labor Committee was formed, under the late Felix Adler's leadership, for nation-wide endeavor. With both these groups we have actively coöperated. The New York Committee has been responsible for effective state legislation establishing a minimum age and physical and educational standards for young workers.

When teeth were put into the law prohibiting the employment of children under fourteen and demanding their attendance at school, we found a family here and there that encouraged shaving for the small boy. Anticipating the physical examination at fourteen, they were under the illusion that hirsute growth would prove that the child was chronologically ready for working papers.

Lack of familiarity with the needs of the child extended into the court itself. The magistrates, inexperienced and moved by thoughtless, kindly impulses, almost uniformly dismissed the case of the illegally employed child, and the protective legislation became a mockery. Two things were done. First, the magistrates were invited to dinner, since we felt that in personal conversation they would learn and remember more than if a pamphlet were sent around. Further, we were able, through the wisdom and generosity of Leo Arnstein, a member of the Child Labor Committee, to pledge the magistrates that the child who really suffered by the enforcement of the law would have relief in the form of a scholarship, regularly given, until he could legally go to work. In addition to assistance for the child and his family, this gave the Committee very practical information upon the home and school situations of children sent to work, legally or otherwise.

The conditions under which children toil are quite as important as the "school-leaving age." The thorough

study of New York canneries made by Pauline Goldmark disclosed the abuse of the children's time, the hard
labor, the long hours, the interference with school attendance.

The possibility of legislation to correct these conditions was complicated by a ruling of the Attorney General, holding that under certain conditions work in the
cannery sheds was agricultural and that the factory law
did not apply to it.   The opinion was the more astonishing since it was delivered after the Attorney
General had had opportunity to review a mass of
evidence showing that children were often required
to work inhuman hours and sometimes all night.   One
well-substantiated though extreme instance was that of
a little boy who, with the knowledge of employer and
parents, had snipped beans from 4 A.M. to 7 P.M.

A measure prohibiting child labor in the canneries
was finally passed.   It seemed to many of us a dis-
couragingly long struggle, for a law that had little
chance of enforcement.

While motoring through a cannery section of the
state after the law was in force, we stopped to converse
with a group of children on their way to school.

"How comes it you are not working in the cannery?"
we asked.

To which a little girl, fresh enough not to be em-
barrassed, replied, "We ain't in the cannery 'cause some
folks in New York won't let us."

Here was reassuring evidence that committee work
is not always an abstract occupation.

I served as chairman of a special committee of the New York Child Labor Committee, which investigated the most popular of the street trades — selling and delivering newspapers. Despite the general belief that newsboys support widowed mothers to whom they bring all their earnings, we found a very different picture. The majority of the parents objected to the ease with which the children could obtain papers to sell, even after there had been a ruling that the child must obtain "the badge" from the school authorities. The parents based their opposition to street selling on the very reasonable arguments that the boys wore out shoe leather, that they kept their earnings and learned to gamble with them, that they found lodgings (often unwholesome ones) outside the home, that they stood in front of theatres and made undesirable acquaintances, and that they learned to "work" sentimental people, particularly those who had just witnessed a "sob" play or movie. We did find, occasionally, the anxious child who brought his money home, where it was much needed; and we were anguished to discover one sick lad who, thinly dressed, had endured late hours on the streets in all weather. A call for the nurse to attend him in the grave illness that resulted disclosed the pitiful circumstances. Unfortunately, the sick-looking newsboy is the most successful at his "trade."

Children may suffer not from voluntary overwork, nor from exploitation, but from the mistaken standards of their parents. The most tragic instance of this in our experience was that of a family group of paper-bag makers. One of our nurses found by accident a family of pathetic children, pasting paper bags in a chilly basement room. When we reproached other children in the house, many of whom were our friends, for not reporting these miserable little toilers, they replied: "We did n't know they lived there! They never came out to play." The five children in the family had all been born in the United States, and were of school age, yet none of them had ever attended school. The mother peddled the bags made in her little sweatshop, and this was the family's meagre income. "If we don't do this we 'll have to ask for charity," was her defense.

Opposition to regulation of the employment of children has been organized and forceful. Employers, where they do not run counter to local opinion, are in some cases not unwilling to resort to questionable practices to hold the children for factory or mill work. The groups formed to protect working children have long seen the need for uniform standards throughout the country. Even when an employer or a community is ready, perhaps eager, to improve conditions, the impulse has been all too often defeated by the pressure of less enlightened competitors. Two attempts to regulate child labor by federal legislation, each in force only a short time, were declared unconstitutional by the Supreme Court—one in 1918, the second in 1922. Finally an "enabling" amendment to the Constitution was adopted by the Congress. It reads: —

Section 1. The Congress shall have power to limit, regulate and prohibit the labor of persons under eighteen years of age.

Section 2. The power of the several states is unimpaired by this article except that the operation of state laws shall be suspended to the extent necessary to give effect to legislation enacted by the Congress.

At this writing, it has been ratified by twenty states, fourteen of them in their 1932–1933 legislative sessions.

President Hoover's Conference on Child Health and Protection, in November 1930, urged general adoption by states of the sixteen-year age minimum for child workers, with an eight-hour day and special regulations for children sixteen to eighteen years old employed in hazardous occupations. This stand, reënforced by various follow-up state conferences, has helped educate the public to the need for acceptable standards.

In March 1933, the recovery programme proposed by President Roosevelt and his associates laid emphasis on the distribution of available work to aid in providing jobs for millions of the unemployed. The anti-child-labor group, headed by the Secretary of Labor, urged as one means to that end that children under sixteen be taken out of the labor market. As a result, the codes of fair competition approved at Washington all bar child labor in the trades affected, though they permit the employment of children between fourteen and sixteen in non-mechanical lines (stores, offices, and so on) when schools are not in session. Various interests — newspapers, theatres, messenger services, and so forth — have sought special exemptions, and the National Child Labor Committee and other groups have actively opposed such attempts to break down the new standard. As I write, comes the welcome ruling by the NRA that no exceptions to the prohibition on child labor are to be granted. Dr. Leo Wolman, chairman of the Labor Advisory Board, states that "when the loss of the child's job means hardship to the family, the Administration has accepted the responsibility for meeting the emergency." Such cases are to be handled either by providing work relief for adults in the family, or by a direct relief grant. And this is social wisdom.

To safeguard further the working child, it is to be hoped that the states will enact into law the White House conference standards; with this should come ratification of the child labor amendment, making possible a national law which will conserve the gains under the emergency acts.

Since the latter part of the nineteenth century, social workers have united in urging the importance of maintaining the family unit. Numerous states now provide relief measures for keeping intact the family group; and in most communities the problems created by the death, invalidism, or desertion of the family breadwinner are not met by severing family ties, except as a last resort.

To a very unusual extent, childless couples in this country have taken, as their own, parentless children. Among the foster parents are many unmarried women and occasionally unmarried men. Admired among the latter was the admiral who adopted five Russian famine orphans and is credited with making them happy in their Washington home. The custom of adoption was borrowed from England, but it has been extended and safeguarded here. Present-day laws require for

legal adoption thorough investigation of the home situation and of the child's health and heredity, and sometimes a trial period to make sure that foster parents
and adopted child are congenial.   New York has several
interesting demonstrations of how wise people organized
for the purpose may help in establishing these "artificial"
families, which are so often rich in their rewards to
both parents and children.   Perhaps the best known
are the Spence School Alumnæ, who now have little
if any difficulty in locating the homeless child in the
promising home, and Dr. Henry Dwight Chapin, who
has long stood out among pediatricians as one of the
earliest advocates of home provision for the child in
preference to even the most careful hospital or other
institutional care.   The Settlement's experiences have
usually been encouraging.

One began with repeated calls from a fireman sta-
tioned at the fire house next door.

"Now look here, Miss Wald," said he.   "We have n't
got a baby.   Can't you get one for us?"

Asked about his trade before he joined the Fire Department, he said that he had been a mosaic worker, and
that he had belonged to the union.

"Did you leave in good standing?"

"I 'll show you the papers!"

The Henry Street nurse in the home district of this
fireman (he lived in Yonkers) visited his place and
reported it immaculate.   The wife came herself to
repeat the husband's plea.   A suitable little girl with the
desired blue eyes was found, all the requirements satisfied, and the baby adopted.   Some months later, while

in Maine, I received a letter with two charming kodak pictures. The fireman wrote: —

DEAR MISS WALD: —

That baby is alright. She is something grand, but she is n't any good to me because my fire house is at the extreme end of one part of the city and my home at the extreme end of the other part and when I come home she 's asleep and my wife won't let me wake her. Could n't you finish the good job and get me transferred to a fire house near my home?

Discussion of this with Fire Commissioner Adamson brought the desired result, and the fireman was happily placed near the home and near the baby.

Progress has been made in the public attitude toward many difficult family adjustments. This finds expression in legislative enactments toward meeting the problems.

The law has stepped in, but not yet adequately, to guard the illegitimate child. Norway has led all the nations in provision for children born out of wedlock, and it is interesting that in North Dakota, where so many Norwegian immigrants have settled, the illegitimate child has the same status in law as the child of a "normal" home.

Stepmothers are not as hated and feared as once they were. I regretfully admit that this injustice to stepmothers had its origin in my beloved fairy tales, where she is usually the villain. I could relate more anecdotes of devoted stepmothers and appreciative stepchildren than I could the reverse. But the law is cognizant of difficulties that do arise.

When the Settlement is brought in as arbitrator in a home where there is a stepfather or stepmother, it is as likely to find fault on the part of the children as of the parents. Sometimes this is because children feel the mother has remarried beneath the family level. One such case, which we were called in to mediate, grew out of the fact that the children insisted on claiming that the new parent was a letter carrier, but alas and alas, this was not true — he was a street sweeper! I cannot say how permanently we salved the wounded dignity of the children, but the sweeper and his wife felt that they had friends.

It is difficult to write upon any aspect of child protection without dwelling upon the superb advances — educational, legislative, administrative — that have been made possible through the stimulus of the U. S. Children's Bureau. That bureau was first urged because of the experience of the Henry Street Settlement, which had abundant evidence every day of the year of the need for an organized, centralized source of information; and because of our conviction that the government, which concerned itself so expertly with sources of material production, had an obligation toward the greatest wealth of the nation: the children. There is hardly a phase of child life that has not been comprehended and improved by the efforts of this agency. Through its scientific studies, its extraordinarily gifted staff, the bureau has presented, as a scientist would present, the injustice to society and to the children of any condition that impairs the health or morals or prevents the education of our youth. The bureau sets a high standard for other agencies, public and private, by the accuracy of its information, the common sense and high integrity that rule its statements, and by the profound knowledge of social conditions that touch upon the life and happiness of the nation's children. The establishment of the bureau, the story of which I have told in full elsewhere,[4] opened a window to show to the whole country — perhaps to the whole world — the value of knowing its children and their needs.

Assurance as to the widespread interest to-day in the Children's Bureau came to me when I discussed its work over the radio in "Collier's Hour." Heavy fan mail does not usually shower upon me after a radio talk, but this time it came in a deluge — within a day or two from near-by communities; a little later from the South and Middle West; and at the end of the week from the Pacific Coast and from towns and rural mail routes up "branch lines."

When in 1930 the dispute arose in the White House conference concerning the proposed division of the bureau's functions, the Biblical illustration of Solomon's test of true motherhood was widely cited. Women seemed to rise *en masse*, insisting that this federal mother was not to see her child dismembered. It was not merely a matter of sentiment: experience and reason have shown the impossibility of understanding even the "normal" child, much less the child in trouble, without bringing together all the elements of his life and environment.

In other chapters of this book I have been specific

[4] *The House on Henry Street.*

about the effects of health education and the measures
that have been taken to ward off disease in favored communities.   But the U. S. Children's Bureau, through
federal and state coöperation, was responsible for one of
the most effective efforts to reduce the maternity and
infant death rate under the measure known as the
Sheppard-Towner Act, in effect from 1922 to 1929.
Behind that splendid and, I regret to say, impermanent
effort lies a colorful story.

One day the mail brought an extraordinary letter
from a woman in Burnt Fork, Wyoming.   It was
lengthy.   It explained first that the husband of the
writer was a renter, that they lived many miles from a
neighbor, that she was appealing to me only because she
had read my articles in the *Atlantic Monthly*, sent her
by a friend in the East, and concluded that I must be
"real folks."   She had one child, and was very unhappy because the doctor had told her she could never
have another.   The previous summer "a man who did
not look fit to care for any child" had "walked in" from
Salt Lake City.   He had a little girl.   Her shoes "must
have been No. 10, and they were almost falling to
pieces.   I took this little girl and she is my daughter,"
wrote the wife of the renter.   Some nights before, she
continued, they had had the worst blizzard ever known
in that part of Wyoming.

"There came a knock at the door, and when we
opened it we saw a man — really a frightened boy.   He
had ridden across country to us, his nearest neighbors,
because the bishop [Mormon] had not been able to get
there to lay his hands on the wife.   The boy was scared.

My husband and I fixed the fire so the house would n't burn down, explained to the children that we would be back as soon as we could, and followed the boy. We got to his house just in time to take the baby. I took the kiver from the poor girl, because she did n't need it any more. I wrapped the baby and took it home with us. The next morning we rode back and buried the poor little mother in a white dress. The reason I am writing to you is because I need help, unless to take help makes my baby a charity case. We need condensed milk, and it costs a great deal because we have got to send so many miles for it. Nobody can pay me for taking care of the baby, but I don't see how we can manage the milk. If you think it 's all right, will you ask someone to do it? Zona Gale, who used to be my neighbor back East, can tell you whether I'm all right, and that I 'm not the kind of a person who would refuse to take care of a child, or ask for help if I could help it."

Needless to say, the condensed milk was provided without impairing the dignity of woman or baby.

Occasional letters passed between us. Then came an excited note: "The doctor was mistaken — I 'm going to have a baby, and where can I learn how to give the best care?"

Of course I recommended the U. S. Children's Bureau, where she could obtain without charge pamphlets which would meet her immediate need. In due time I received a letter from the bureau, inquiring whether there was any nursing service that could be made available to a woman at Burnt Fork, Wyoming. Alas, I was obliged to answer that at that time the nearest visiting nurse was in Salt Lake City, sixty difficult miles away. However, the matter was not allowed to drop. Finally a woman physician, long associated with Hull House, learned of the dilemma. "I might as well take this time for a vacation in Wyoming," she said.

The experience of this generous doctor in Wyoming was the foundation of the Sheppard-Towner Act, which made it possible for women in lonely places to get maternity help. All those who know the plight of isolated mothers and their babies regret that the measure has lapsed because of the failure to provide federal funds for grants-in-aid to the states. However, a few states, having had experience with its beneficence, continue the programme at their own expense. It is important that it should be resumed and extended, for our record in infant and maternal mortality is a disgraceful one. More than 150,000 of our babies under a year of age die annually — and many of them are sacrificed to ignorance or to lack of reasonable medical or nursing facilities.

Obviously it is not possible to detail here the manifold needs and efforts for bringing the protecting arm of the law about the children. But certain fundamental truths are clear even in so limited a review as this.

As a people, we have begun to see the implications of the old saying that the children of to-day are the adults of to-morrow. Courts have now been given the power to regulate the custody of children, to inquire into guardianship, to sift charges against the "wayward," to pass upon intemperate custom. We have made progress in safeguarding the child at work and the child whose home conditions are difficult or unusual. We have learned that in the vast majority of cases the child in a family circle is more secure — healthier in body, mind, and spirit — than the child in an institution.

While we have every reason to be happy over the gains that have been made in protecting children, we must not delude ourselves that all is well.

We have made progress because of the idealism and hard work of men and women, many among them still young and ardent, inspired to carry on toward new goals. They find encouragement in accomplishment and in the growing number of their fellow workers — recruits from among their contemporaries and the younger generation. The nation has become the centre of the hope and faith of all who see a more satisfying world through safeguarding children from cruelty, exploitation, ignorance, and maladjustment, giving them freedom to grow into strong and happy human beings.

IX

PROHIBITION AND THE FOUR MILLION

WHEN I try to present the problem of prohibition as we have learned to know it, and to study the effect upon our community of the amendment, to analyze as far as possible the pronouncements of those who favored and those who opposed it, I realize that they have made their decisions — as I have — from their own contacts, from their points of actual observation. For forty years my lot has been cast with New Yorkers, not of the "Four Hundred," but of the "Four Million," and it is of this latter group that I venture to speak. Those in the army of the repealists who were called to the colors see things from their own environment. Those of us who come out frankly in our testimony favoring the prohibition amendment view the matter also from our actual points of observation. There can be no doubt that different elements of society are affected differently by results of laws whose enactment touches the life of all. The surface differences are obvious; the evidence is not so clear that the fundamental result of social experiment and social change differs greatly on Park Avenue and on Henry Street.

The conflict over the prohibition experiment has been for the most part between people who, like myself, saw a better life among the families of the wage earners while the amendment was in force, and, on the other side, those who hated "hypocrisy" in their set and what they called the "invasion" of their personal liberty, and who saw the source of all crime in the bootlegger, even though he was often indirectly in their employ. It was frequently asserted that there would be little opposition to a law permitting the sale of light wines and beer, but sanction and enforcement do not seem practical, and there was in the minds of those who seriously studied the bootlegger the fact that he prospered, not on light wines and beer, but on the stronger drinks; further, it is generally agreed that the notorious hip flask contained neither light wine nor beer. To one who has had many years of friendship with wage earners, it is not surprising that the technical point of view should give way to the bearing of law and custom on the families which do not have the protection of steady incomes adequate to their needs.

In any discussion of our experience with a federal prohibition law, it would seem to be as important as it is difficult to keep in perspective not only the changes brought about, favorable or unfavorable, in individual, family, and community life, but also the background of the American endeavor toward temperance and a controlled liquor traffic, the differences in racial tradition and custom among our people, and the attitude and practice of other countries.

The trend of discussion would often lead one to believe that the Eighteenth Amendment suddenly sprang into being like a startling djinn called forth by the rubbing of a legislative lamp. As a matter of fact, several of the states came into the Union originally as "dry" territory, and others early in their history forbade the manufacture or sale of alcoholic beverages within their borders. Previous to prohibition, many communities regulated or controlled the sale of liquor, and we need to be reminded that at the time the Eighteenth Amendment went into effect, on January 16, 1920, two thirds of the states had already adopted prohibition by popular vote, about 90 per cent of the land area was at least theoretically dry, and nearly 70 per cent of the American people nominally lived under a dry regimen.

Often, however, local laws were weakened by the liquor traffic in neighboring states and the ease with which liquor crossed the borders. Despite the stories that are told of violations in Maine and elsewhere, under state prohibition, business men and other leading citizens declared that industry profited by the absence of the saloon.

In the Scandinavian countries I remained long enough one summer to become acquainted with the "Gothenburg" licensing system, under which limited quantities of liquor may be purchased for home consumption.

But home drinking in these countries is associated more with harmless gayety, — betrothals, weddings, birthday anniversaries, and the like, — and I found it a painful contrast to the American saloon, its relationship to politics, and its disastrous destruction of family life.   And even under the much-quoted "Gothenburg" system alcohol was feared.   It was interesting to find that in Bergen, Norway, the façade of a building where liquor could be purchased — by no means a saloon in our sense — was covered by a painting of a little girl entreating her father not to spend his wage, but to bring it home.

On the Continent, doubtless the French prohibition of absinthe more nearly parallels America's attempt to withhold strong drink.

And if prohibition was no new thing to the vast majority of us in 1920, similarly the American people were not unfamiliar with the influence of liquor interests on public life, though one hears the "bootlegger" and the "racketeer" spoken of as though they were the first, in the name of King Rum, to lay unclean hands on governmental agencies.   The whole success of the bootlegger's trade depends on corruption, but this was as true before prohibition as it was later.   On Henry Street, though not a neighborhood of heavy drinking, we have been all too close to the practical aspects of this traffic.   The saloon opposite us caused us trouble for years.   After the prohibition amendment went into effect, it left our neighborhood and we were accused of being the cause of its downfall.   Paul's notorious place on Henry Street was driven from the neighborhood after many battles, and largely through the efforts of the Jacob Riis House, the settlement close by. But there was a house in Charlton Street, very near a school, where trucks often stopped and cases of liquor were unloaded. Neighbors on both sides of this house saw customers going in and often saw police officers partaking of refreshment. I had correspondence about this place, and more than once higher city officials came to me to tell me what they were doing to stop the nuisance; but it never stopped. It was not an uncommon sight to see an officer on the sidewalk ensuring safe delivery of "the goods."

Throughout this country's political history there have been many instances of the part played by liquor interests, a part far more important than the local political control with which every large city is familiar. Tammany in New York, "the machine," Democratic or Republican, in other cities, all had their "contacts" with the "legitimate" liquor interests prior to prohibition as well as with the illicit liquor trade of recent years. Many people still living recall the nation's humiliation over the disclosure of the "Whiskey Ring" in the Grant Administration. In all the pre-prohibition periods of our national history, intelligent leaders have cried out against the corruption of public life by the liquor traffic, which, they always held, threatened the success of the American experiment with democracy.

Paralleling this there has been repeated resistance to attempted "interference" with the free use of liquor or individual right to trade in it. As far back as 1791, Americans protested against a federal liquor tax, and in

1794 the Whiskey Rebellion, resulting in wounds and death, followed an attempt to collect taxes on liquor distilled from grain by farmers who found it easier to transport a few bottles of whiskey than sacks of grain over the almost impassable roads of the period. Denunciations of this "interference with individual right" have a familiar sound to those who listened to arguments for the repeal of the Eighteenth Amendment nearly a century and a half later. The same "rugged individualism" of the frontier has always hampered and often defeated honest and efficient federal revenue officers in remote mountain regions where neighbors help protect the "moonshiners."

In trying to keep in perspective our attempt to bring about "total abstinence" by law, it is well to bear in mind the sources of that effort. Charles and Mary Beard, in their *Rise of American Civilization*, remind us: "It was safe to venture a guess that the desire of business men for efficiency and safety in labor was as potent in bringing about the new régime as the wanton lust of moralists determined to impose their own standards upon the nation."

On this point the testimony of industrial employers and of social workers is in agreement. We may differ as to whether national prohibition did or did not unduly infringe the personal liberties of the people. Not all were in agreement in viewing the definition of an alcoholic content under the Volstead Act as either satisfactory or scientific. But those who best know the wage earner and his problems are united in their inability to forget (and it should never be forgotten) the place the

SPEAK-EASY NIGHTS

saloon occupied in the lives of the great majority of the men and their families.

It was on Saturday nights that the real power of the saloons was most obvious. Trucks lined up at the curbs while their drivers went inside with their pay envelopes. That Saturday night scene disappeared from one end of the country to the other, and with it went the Sunday brawls and the tragic Monday mornings, when in factory and workshop women appealed for advances on their husbands' wage because Mike or Jim or Tony had left the contents of his pay envelope in the saloon.

Perhaps few to-day remember the "Sabbath Lighters," the old drunken women who hung around Jewish neighborhoods waiting to be called into orthodox homes on the holy day when it is a sin for the faithful to handle fire. The meagre job secured for these old derelicts the means for a weekly debauch, and, their pittance earned, they would go reeling along the streets, mocked and stoned by jeering boys, pitiable, repellent spectacles. They have disappeared. The young generation that grew up after the amendment went into effect never saw them, and knows no more of them than it knows of "Suicide Hall" or places like "McGuirk's." These were the numberless "joints" that flourished brazenly along the Bowery and other streets throughout the city. Though every artifice was employed by schools, social workers, and conscientious parents to keep the young away from them, the proprietors could well afford to smile at the feeble gestures of the would-be protectors of the young.

I have gone to the owners of these and of similar dance halls to protest against the open bar, occasionally offering a goodly sum to have it closed while the dance was on. The dances, mind you, were for the very young, and the halls were rented for a small sum because dancing was only incidental to the profitable sale of liquor. Every device to draw the crowds by bright lights and gay music and jolly company was cunningly employed to promote the desire to drink. Indeed, it was often a remarkable example of intuitive use of the psychology of suggestion: the exposed bar, the grand march stopping to exchange banter with the bartender, the habit of treating, the conspicuous aproned waiters, the brief dances, the long waits, the overheated, unventilated rooms which increased thirst. Presents of bottles of wine to the "ladies," a keg or two of beer to the "gentlemen," were often made to start the hilarity. The brewers were in many instances the real owners of the halls, as they were of the saloons, paying the license or holding the mortgage like a sword of Damocles over the head of a nominal proprietor.

Clinton Hall, built as a centre for social and trade-union purposes in our neighborhood, held a license as insurance against the accusation of being "for reform." But those who attended a Clinton Hall meeting or dance were obliged to leave the pleasant crowd and go down two flights of stairs to buy a drink. The sale of liquor in this hall was infinitesimal.

A saloon, notorious in an uptown neighborhood, closed after the amendment was ratified, and was rented by us for one of our nursing centres. We liked the humor of keeping on the door "Family Entrance" for the maternity cases.

Let me tell here about the Currys, not because their story is unique, but because it is typical. Mrs. Curry was a gay young Irish girl. Her husband was gay, too, and they had jolly times together. Then he took to the bottle, and their home became the home of a drunkard. He was a generous and well-meaning man toward his family, but treats and invitations from "the boys" were irresistible. After the saloons were closed and the treats no longer offered, this really kindly fellow found satisfaction in his home and children. His wage was sufficient for the family needs when it was not squandered at the saloon, and before long he bought a radio. Curry does n't understand music, but he enjoys it, and occasionally he and his wife go to the Stadium concerts. The whole family life is changed — the day-by-day experience and the outlook for the children. Such a family history could be repeated in substance again and again from the annals of our neighbors and the experience of our nurses in every section of the city.

On the other hand, we realize that the hip flask and the speak-easies became familiar to a large number. Unfortunately the elders all too often failed to furnish examples of obedience to law, adopting the time-honored excuse that law is good for some people, but not necessary for others.

Exaggerated stories of drunkenness among young people and of sex delinquency resulting from it went the rounds. Stories about drinking among college and high school students under prohibition and of an unwholesome preoccupation with sex have frequently been told as though such behavior were unknown prior to prohibition. This unfortunately was not the case, as many well know. Further confusion is due to the habit of comparing the prohibition period with the pre-War decade, rather than with the same period in "wet" European countries or with the years here following previous wars. In every post-war decade there has been a marked lowering in the moral tone of the country, much deplored by thoughtful writers of the period.

In contrast to innumerable households where the bootlegger was accepted as a natural adjunct to the administration of the home, many fathers and mothers, even though some of them were not in sympathy with enforced prohibition, were law-abiding. They believed that they could not, should not, choose the laws they would obey where there were children in the family.

I challenged one father for taking whiskey to his boy in college. The boy, incidentally, was in training, and neither he nor his friends opened the bottle. The father's defense was that he wanted the boy to drink "good stuff." But to "treat" his son from his own bootlegger's wares could have given him no real security, since many famous labels were imitated in little printing shops in New York and affixed to bottles of adulterated stock.

The same spirit of bravado that made heroes of lawbreakers from Jesse James and other Wild West robbers to Gerald Chapman and "Two Gun" Crowley played its part in the defiance of the prohibition law by young people, and perhaps by their elders as well. Our national weakness for "fads" must have influenced our attitude toward the amendment. At a dinner of distinguished men and women in London, all the guests agreed that when they were in the United States socially or to lecture the topics of conversation were limited to calories and prohibition. Now that the excitement and adventure of being lawbreakers, fortified by moral theories, have cooled, they would find a large range of interest as measured by dinner-table conversation. Perhaps because no enthusiasm has a long life in America, I am reminded of "Mr. Dooley's" remark that when our interest kindles it is "a bonfire on a cake of ice."

But whatever may have been the effect of the hip flask on the youth of the fraternity and sorority houses, the private "prep" schools, and the country clubs, drinking during prohibition was far less general among the children of the Four Million than many advocates of repeal believe and assert.

In 1930, when I was collecting first-hand data on the situation, Karl Hesley, long in charge of our social activities at the Settlement, told me that in a typical year while the amendment was in force only one flask was discovered at a Henry Street dance.

Miss Helen Hall, then the able head resident of the University Settlement in Philadelphia, and now Head Worker at the Henry Street Settlement,[1] thus compared the prohibition era with pre-prohibition days: —

At our dance hall at University House, where between two and three hundred young people dance every Monday

[1] Since August 1, 1933.

night, formerly there was seldom a night that some of the dancers did not have to be carried out and their friends called to take them home. This has not happened for over two years.

In Chicago, during recent years, social workers and specially appointed policemen have kept close watch on dance-hall conditions. The carrying of a hip flask was interpreted as coming under the law, and every boy or man who paid an entrance fee was searched by the officer. If a flask was found, the contents were poured down the sewer in the presence of the owner. Miss Addams stated that in an examination of 4500 men only three flasks were found.

A working woman I know was in favor of repeal, because she held that "prohibition just made things worse."

I said to her, "When you go to work in the mornings, do you see the sights of pre-prohibition days?"

"You mean the men and women that were thrown out of saloons sleeping it off in the gutter? No, I don't see that any more. And the vomiting all over the sidewalks in the early morning — I don't see that."

"And how about the young people in your family, your nieces and nephews?" I persisted.

"Oh, them — they take a drink now and then. But when I talk about the saloons and all that, they don't know what I'm talking about. But just the same, you got a right to a drink if you want it."

We were encouraged but not satisfied with evidences of better conditions among wage earners under the prohibition régime that were brought to the attention of social workers. To investigate and assemble reliable information on such changes in family life as might credit or discredit the Eighteenth Amendment, the national organization of settlements in 1926 appointed a committee of which I was chairman. As an assurance that we did not seek propaganda for either side, the study was financed by contributions from those opposed to the experiment and those who had faith in it, and committee and staff included "wets," "drys," and "doubters." Martha Bensley Bruère directed the study, and after our questionnaire had been sent to some three hundred settlements she made supplementary visits of inquiry to representative cities in every section of the country. The findings are therefore more significant than those of the usual questionnaire survey. The testimony there brought together is of continuing interest and importance, and the chapter headed "What We Found Out" is well worth reading even now.[2] The summary concludes: —

Wherever there is a Nordic-American population which for several generations has not been in close contact with the newer immigrations or the cosmopolitanism of the great cities, there prohibition works. . . . Wherever there are large unassimilated foreign populations accustomed to the making and use of alcoholic drinks and also an eager market for their product, as in the great ports and the industrial cities, there the law is halting and veering and difficult to apply.

[2] *Does Prohibition Work?* National Federation of Settlements, Committee on Prohibition; edited by Martha Bensley Bruère (Harper).

But the reports do show that all the things hoped for by the advocates of prohibition are being realized in some places, and that even where the law is least observed, some of them have come true.

It is a matter of regret that the statisticians and the scientists have not been able to agree on the facts as to increase or decrease in consumption, and even as to the effect of alcohol on health and longevity. Dr. Irving Fisher and Dr. Haven Emerson, in their interpretation of the workings of the amendment, apparently speak a different language from that of some other distinguished economists and physicians. Figures are hurled forward by both sides in the controversy, the same statistics occasionally being mustered in by both camps. Dr. Emerson, unflinching in his courage and of preëminent scientific stature, contributes a stimulating discussion of this point in an article headed, "Can Wets and Drys Bear the Whole Truth?" [3]

Our own records show that in 1931, among 60,000 patients, our nurses did not have a single diagnosis of alcoholism. Dr. Maximilian Schulman, for many years in charge of the home service of the Vanderbilt Clinic in New York City, says that cases of acute and chronic alcoholism practically disappeared from the medical service of the Vanderbilt Clinic, whereas in pre-prohibition days they were very common; and he adds, "Whatever prohibition may have done for the idle rich, it certainly has done well for the laboring poor."

In the great volume of relief during the present de-

[3] *Survey Graphic*, August 1933.

pression the question of unemployment because of
drunkenness has not been raised. In 1928–1929, the
last year for which comparative figures are available,
the records of the foremost private welfare agency in
New York City show that only one out of eleven families registered drink as a factor in their dependence;
before prohibition, when the saloon was in flower, the
figure was one out of four. It is only very rarely that
drunkenness has of late years appeared as a problem
among the families we know. One instance was young
Dan Flanagan.

Dan Flanagan the elder worked for many years in a
famous hat factory. He was a skilled workman, but
despite his good wages his wife was forced to take in
fine laundry to make up a deficit in the family budget
due to drink. Dan died early, and with her son life
was renewed for my friend. Some years passed, years of
hard work but of decent comfort and of hope for little
Mrs. Flanagan. Then she came to see me, draggled
and poor once more. Young Dan had followed in his
father's footsteps. "The worst of it is, young Dan
gets drunk on beer," said the mother. And when she
saw that I was mystified as to why this should make
any difference she explained, "Oh, you don't understand
how much more it costs to get drunk on beer!"

The question of additional public income played a
large part in the impetus the repeal movement received, nationally and in the states. This argument, I
may say, was not appreciated by our neighbors. For
when the beer parade marched up Fifth Avenue, led by
Mayor "Jimmy" Walker, some of the women said:

"Who's going to buy the beer? We think the Mayor should lead a bread parade."

Other social workers joined me in signing a letter to the *New York Times,* shortly after the 1932 national election, defining our position in regard to modification or repeal of the prohibition amendment: —

As social workers we are naturally vitally concerned with the question of the modification or repeal of the Eighteenth Amendment, for just as in the old days our experience afforded us tragic, first-hand evidence of the evils of the saloon and the liquor traffic, so to-day we cannot be insensible to some of the unfortunate by-products of this well-intentioned effort to control a national menace.

Though few settlement workers participated in the orthodox temperance movement and though we felt that the definition of the Volstead Act was unscientific and potentially dangerous because of its extreme mandate, yet we came to approve the Eighteenth Amendment because through it conditions among the people we know best in underprivileged neighborhoods have greatly improved. . . .

We believe that the new mandate from the people as interpreted by the recent election demands the wisest statesmanship, the profoundest social study, before we risk a resumption of the practically uncontrolled sale of drink. Nobody advocates the return of the saloon, but unless every preparation is made for the safeguarding of the sale of liquor, there is no hope but that the saloon, whether called so or not, will be upon us. . . .

We who are deeply integrated in neighborhoods where many face a tragic renewal of conditions destructive of home life and of respect and dignity, we have no panacea to offer. But because we believe that the greatest safeguards are inherent in the stern protection of the manufacture, sale, and distribution of liquor, we offer our experience as to the possibility of accomplishing this. As social workers we are realists, and we wish to state our case and add such knowledge as we may have to the study of this important question.

It is cause for deep regret that sincere temperance advocates who made such great progress before the prohibition era accepted a national prohibition law as a cure-all. With the enactment of the amendment, those who favored total abstinence stopped their educational efforts and in fact rested their arms on the legislation. This is the sadder to record because the trend in America, as in other countries, was toward temperance. There is now opportunity to start afresh, to substitute better methods for the extreme measures that failed, and to win the support of all sincere social thinkers, irrespective of the wing to which they formerly adhered. It is of vital importance that there should be effective education on the whole subject — not an emotional appeal, but a clear, scientific, and interesting presentation, neither whitewashing any theory nor omitting any pertinent fact. Americans generally should realize, as they were beginning to do before the hue and cry over enforcement confused the issues, that the use of alcoholic beverages and the manufacture and sale of liquors are matters of grave import; men and women who have a deep concern with social progress should be ready to express themselves intelligently and without bias. We need not only study by experts but presentations as vivid and clear as the Russian Primer,[4]

[4] *New Russia's Primer,* by M. Ilin (Houghton Mifflin).

an outstanding lesson in making a serious and complex subject attractive and convincing to children, to adults of limited educational opportunity, as well as to informed citizens.

In Russia's awareness of the harm liquor can do in time of public emergency there is another lesson for us. I had heard that in "the ten days that shook the world" machine guns were turned on the wine cellars of the Tsar and the stocks destroyed. Anna Louise Strong asked Trotsky whether this was true. He said that it was; that he had ordered it, though he regretted the necessity, since there was great need for good wine in the hospitals. But he had thought this measure necessary because he felt that if the men had access to liquor it would be impossible to "carry the revolution."

It is unfortunate that the Eighteenth Amendment aroused so much conflict, and that its enforcement was confused with the problems of a post-war period, of an unprecedented boom and depression. These twelve years did not *prove* anything. If, however, the *interest* that has been aroused can be conserved for the least intoxicating drinks, and if there is no relaxation in the determination to keep out the saloon, something will have been gained. One ventures to hope that we have acquired, by this painful experience, real insight and a programme that is proof against the faults of the extremists on either side. It is hard to underscore sufficiently the need for a procedure that will guard against the flagrant wrongs proponents of repeal are inclined to minimize. Sincere motivation should erect dependable barriers against the long and repeated corruptions that have always accompanied the sale of drink, and against the attacks of unyielding individualists, thereby making it possible to forget the charges and countercharges and to unite in a programme that will effectively control the manufacture, sale, and distribution of what a woman out of bitter experience called "those contentious fluids." Government control seems to be the only measure that can eliminate them. We have gone through years of trial and tribulation. There is hope that, with economic and political changes which may be called revolutionary, there will come an agreement on how to accomplish such control.

Without repeating the arguments, without growing wistful over what might have been done, we must face the challenge of the repeal, united in a sound policy that will forbid the repetition of disasters which are real.

If repeal does not bring back the saloon, if the new dispensation guards against the pitfalls that another generation knew, — the tragedy of the drunkard's home, the sacrifice of family life, the handicapped children, the debased standards of morals and health, — those of us who have cared so profoundly will share in the rejoicing of those who have "won" in this contest.

X

THE LEAN YEARS

To workers in settlements, as to others in daily contact with wage earners, are first revealed the signs of the times affecting their security. As the periods of depression come over us, there is no sudden avalanche, but a creeping daily change — shortening hours of work, an increasing number of dismissals, wage cuts, and the uneasiness which none can comprehend unless they have learned to recognize and share it. It permeates a neighborhood like a thickening fog of anxiety and fear.

Increasingly in the winter of 1928–1929, months before the stock-market crash, we were made aware of the foreboding among our neighbors. In the kindergarten one morning, when the little ones were sitting around the table drinking their milk, I said, "What do

you think you are going to be when you grow up?"
There was no very active response, and to prod them
I said, "When I was a little girl I thought I should like
to be a carpenter — the shavings are so curly and the
carpenters who came to our house were such nice folks."
Whereupon a four-year-old who sat there, his head in
his hand, a sober expression on his little face, answered,
"Miss Wald, the carpenter that lives in our house ain't
got any work."

The nurses' daily records are delicate barometers of
conditions. This was brought home to me once as I
watched our statistician sticking her pins in the map
that shows the current cases of pneumonia, and observed an increasing number of blue pins in the Syrian
quarter. Inquiring into this, I was told that the children of the kimono workers then on strike were probably getting less milk and good nourishment, and hence
their resistance was lowered.

Signs of the gathering storm multiplied. Within a
brief period a succession of individuals came to ask for
work, and that stimulated us to further inquiry. In
January 1928, we discussed this with our intimate circle.
In February 1929, eight months before the "boom"
collapsed, we summoned our colleagues to a meeting,
just as, on the first declaration of war in August
1914, we called a group to come together in solemn
conference.

There was general agreement that times were increasingly hard in the neighborhoods where small wage earners lived, with mounting numbers of men and women
"laid off." But at that time the public was absorbed in

"the greatest period of prosperity the world has ever seen," and the storm signals were unheeded.

As troubles grew, we realized that in respect to the disaster to individuals and to the community these desperate years were to prove even more serious to American workers than the War. Families were broken by war, and homes knew terrible griefs — the sacrifice of youth, the lost anchors of safety and security. But all these disasters also befall the people when there is no work, no family income, when youth is sacrificed because its hopes, its dignity, its ambitions, crumble away, and there is no sense of common cause, of a goal to be attained, to glorify the sacrifice. Homes were swept away during the War. Pitiful they were, those fallen roofs and broken walls that I saw in France. But, though less tragic to the onlooker, such depression as we have been experiencing has meant the devastation of homes without number, simple as well as luxurious, built up with high hope and with confidence in the ability of the breadwinner to support the family and to help the children to a higher estate.

Since 1893, the year of my first acquaintance with the Henry Street neighborhood, there have been repeated periods of depression and consequent unemployment. That first unforgettable winter plunged us into abysses of need and helplessness never dreamed of by young crusaders. In the early morning, before we had time to put the kettle on, people began their tramp up our five flights, and the procession continued after our nursing rounds were ended till the last minute of the night, before we sank into fatigued sleep. They came begging us to help them find work, or at least to give them a ticket entitling them to a few days of the "made work" which was being provided as a relief measure.

The help for the unemployed that year was not, of course, so well organized or so effective as the united efforts of the better-trained workers in the present period. And it was tragic then to see the battle between the desperate need of the situation and the dear traditions of so many of our neighbors — more frequently met with forty years ago than now.

A tailor who lived near us and who was devoted to his home and to his wife, the daughter of a rabbi of distinction in the old country, was out of work for many months. There was, of course, a large family, and the usual accompaniment of illness. But even under this burden of pressing need the man finally did not feel that he could continue to keep the "made work" which was the family's sole dependence, because it meant labor on the Sabbath, and that was a desecration. He looked worn and anxious as he told of this decision. But in the midst of our troubled conference his face brightened and he said, "We know, with all our trials, that the Lord has not forsaken us, for we are going to have another baby." And he was further assured that the Lord was on his side when, exerting myself to find some solution for that desperate household, I introduced him to an employer in Passaic, New Jersey, who offered a job and demanded no religious sacrifice to hold it.

The House on Henry Street has seen five major depressions in its forty years — 1893, 1907, 1914, 1921, and the years since 1929. No depression has touched in magnitude the situation of to-day, which must be described, not as critical, but as desperate. During different crises I have served on committees appointed to work out measures of protection against future disasters. The forces have never been so well organized as they are to-day to avoid waste motions, to mobilize resources, to prevent overlapping. But those who have been closest to the chief sufferers know best how inadequate have been even these heroic efforts to meet the most elementary need. And perhaps veterans of experience realize with special clarity the price that must be paid for a break of such magnitude in our economic and social life.

As one sums up the effects of unemployment on the individual and the community, it seems to me that the loss of the dignity of man is the first and most tragic. With this are bound up the loss of home, of ties, of position, the humiliation of the long bread lines, the appeal to relief agencies, the overwhelming sense of failure.

Next I should put, as a result of loss of home, a further break in housing standards, with families herding together for shelter rather than for a home. From that comes loss of family unity, of self-respect, of ambition and pride.

Under the strain of prolonged unemployment, irritations and loss of personality are inevitable even among the heroic.

The people most troubled are often marked by an inexplicable patience, or, it may be, apathy. Perhaps because of lack of leadership, the little groups which have assembled to protest against delay in relief or against methods of relief have had little to contribute. If there is willingness to discuss with them the difficulty of satisfactory relief methods with available resources, their protest melts away. This was illustrated in the attitude of Washington authorities toward the "armies" which demanded relief through the bonus payment in two successive winters — a menace to public health and public dignity, a tragic and absurd display of armed brutality one year; and the next, 1933, the remnant of the "army" well ordered and immediately responsive to considerate treatment.

Finally, this prolonged period of unemployment has forced upon young people the conviction that society, which helped rear and educate them, has no place for them.

The most obvious antisocial effect of unemployment is the breaking up of the family. Social workers long familiar with the vicissitudes of those whose margin between income and expenditure is narrow are impressed by the passionate desire, even from unexpected sources, to cling together that they may maintain family life, that the household may go on. One instance to illustrate: —

A neighbor, a teamster with good wages, was a man of questionable habits until he married a girl of exemplary character. When their baby came, no one who owns a shooting lodge in Scotland or a villa in Florida could feel more pride and satisfaction than this young couple evidenced in moving into an apartment with a bathroom. The room was not only a modern convenience to them, but a long step forward in standard of living and self-respect. The housekeeping was immaculate, but special care was lavished on the bathroom, and no visitor departed without being shown its glories. In the winter of 1930–1931, there was no work for the teamster, and, hoping against hope, we lent the young people rent each month for three months. But recovery did not come, and they were forced to move to cheaper rooms, of course with unkept halls and unkempt janitor. Quickly came the next step down — the demoralization of overcrowding under the necessity of sharing with another couple the rent of the miserable little place. The whole level, not only of housing, but of cleanliness, recreation, personal pride, manners, slumped — as in the days of the Terror in France, when so many heads went under the guillotine, and no to-morrow seemed likely or worth anyone's waiting for.

During that same winter we knew of many instances of three families herded into one apartment. In one such household there were in three rooms seven children and five adults, among them two pregnant women.

And yet our neighbors never hesitated to share their meagre quarters when need arose. The day after a young mother came home from the hospital with her first-born, the nurse called to teach her how to give the baby its bath. To her amazement, she found two newborn babies and a second mother, a young girl who was a stranger to her. This girl had occupied the bed next to the nurse's patient in the ward, and had confided to her that she had no home and no friends to whom she could go when she left the hospital. Her neighbor in the ward therefore invited her to share her tiny tenement quarters. "I can't do much for her," she said apologetically to the nurse, "but I can put a roof over her head." The husband gave up his half of the family bed to the stranger and slept on a narrow couch, and the extra baby slept in the kitchen in the carriage proudly provided for the child of the house. But there was only good will shown to the guest, and a determination to "make out the best we can." I am glad to add a cheering footnote to this story. The husband, so long out of work, has at last obtained a good job, and the young girl also secured employment and has been able to go her way.

When we first lived in a neighborhood of small wage earners, to see on the sidewalk the furniture of a family dispossessed for nonpayment of rent was an everyday affair. Gradually the welfare agencies freed one neighborhood after another from that humiliating evidence of inadequate and tardy relief. It is a matter of pride in the Settlement that there was only one such instance in the winter of 1931–1932 in our immediate neighborhood, and that was through an unforeseeable slip in procedure. But during the continued depression this problem has grown beyond the power of the relief agencies in some sections, and it is now beyond us. The frequent sight of the belongings of the shattered household could, without great stretch of imagination, be compared with the ruined homes we saw in the occupied territory of France. But in this emergency, as in so many others, co-operation is forthcoming from the neighbors whenever possible.

Mrs. D —— went to the hospital to be delivered of her first child. In her absence the "dispossess" was served. Her husband disappeared, taking most of the household goods with him. This, let me hasten to add, was not an example of the "shiftless poor." The wife had taken a four-year commercial course after graduating from a Chicago high school; the husband was a licensed teacher. Desperate would have been the plight of the young mother when she returned from the hospital had it not been for a neighbor who opened her door to Mrs. D —— and the baby. The neighbor herself was receiving relief, but she shared what she had with the deserted, homeless wife and child. The nurse secured such supplementary help as she could for the household. The most delicate consideration is being shown Mrs. D —— by her hostess. But we hope the kind neighbor will soon be relieved of this burden, which she ought not to bear; the initiative will not come from her.

The folk feeling, always at first limited to immediate kith and kin, is widened through sympathy, and the recent years have brought forth, as does every time of stress and strain, not only quick sympathy, but immediate sharing. No ceremonial or convention waits upon the act. Compassion is a basic element when people are thrown together, and too much cannot be said of the simplicity with which our neighbors give and take.

It is at the opposite social pole that one most frequently finds those who frankly refuse to be involved in other people's troubles. At a dinner party in the second winter of the depression I found myself sitting beside a man who told me that he did not care to hear stories of need, that he never read the appeals which came to his bank or to him personally, that he was deaf to their urgency. And when examples of the help of the needy to one another were cited, he complacently retorted that this was inevitable, "because they see it around them all the time." He seemed to pride himself on his deafness, and to be all unaware of the death of the spirit within him.

Under the strain of unemployment and the anxiety and hardship it brings into the home, the wage earner's rebellion against his predicament or his boredom with the long, empty days not infrequently expresses itself in outbursts of temper. In one such home, the ambulance doctor, summoned by our nurse, diagnosed the mother's illness as "starvation complicated by follicular tonsillitis." And the kindly young physician added, "If I have to make many more diagnoses like this I'll be a chicken-hearted fool." The husband, a skilled artisan, had been with the same firm for nine years. Then his employers failed, and for nearly a year he had had no job except a few weeks of "work relief" at a third of his former wage rate. In apologizing to the nurse for rudeness to her and to his family, the man said, "I don't mind being hungry myself, but it's hard to see the wife and kids without enough to eat. And sometimes you get mad and holler just because you feel so bad."

These trying days have been a challenge to the settlements to keep life as balanced as possible, particularly for young people who, having sometimes been educated at great sacrifice, find themselves unwanted. Home conditions have gone beyond reasoning, and they are often reproved for not finding work, with barbed reminders of what others have done. Henry Street has participated in and initiated measures to serve the people, particularly youth, in danger of quagmires from which it might be impossible to bring release. The dances, the music, the club meetings, the gayeties, have never been so strenuously pursued as during these lean years.

One evening, a hot August night, when the children of the neighborhood were playing games and singing in the street, I stopped to talk with three girls walking arm in arm. Young and at the romantic age, it seemed there must be something better for them to do than to walk up and down this hot and crowded street, where children and garbage cans on the sidewalk made even a stroll difficult. I knew there was a dance on the roof of our Playhouse to which ten cents would admit them. To these young girls of dance age I said, "Why are n't you at the party to-night?" In chorus they answered, "We 're out of work. We have n't got ten cents." There was a committee meeting at eight-thirty the next morning, and the price of the dances was adjusted to conform to the means of those who most needed the pleasure.

Because of urgent pressure for the most primitive needs of the people, food and shelter, the essentials of recreation are in danger of being overlooked or even considered indecorous when family cupboards are bare of bread. One truly anxious friend questioned the time and money, however reasonable in amount, allocated to pleasure and recreation in the Settlement budget. But she readily withdrew her objections when the plight of the unemployed boys and girls was described. Few people who have brought up their young under comfortable circumstances have failed to see the importance of a wholesome atmosphere for youth, but they have not always realized that the same rules of control and protection they know to be essential apply to those who live in congested rooms, who hear the doleful tales of their kinsfolk and neighbors, and who may not have even the cheapest movie as a release.

The human side of unemployment as seen by social workers is perhaps best expressed in the studies, the source book of materials, and the coördinated statements by the settlements. Helen Hall's research and writing as chairman of the Unemployment Committee of the National Federation of Settlements illustrate our desire for reliable facts and our unwillingness to allow the human interests involved to be overlooked.

One cannot yet reckon the final cost of this depression. The nurses' records show that it takes an increasingly long time these days for children to recover from what would not have been considered serious illness in happier times. Convincing arguments as to the future values of a healthy childhood, familiar to those interested in child protection and culture, become nightmares when we think of the harvest ahead, when these real victims of depression try to build their adult health and strength on the poor preparation of these years. One cannot estimate the loss by mortality statistics. The sick and

BACK YARDS

feeble do not always die.   One is reminded of Dr. Osler's famous observation, "People seldom die of the diseases they have."   Malnutrition, bad housing, anxiety, and the other evils of depression are fraught with consequences that cannot be appraised.

One of the most dramatic phases of the depression as it affects youth is the large number of boys, and some girls, too, who have gone "on the loose," tramping back and forth across the continent, riding freights, "hitchhiking," and often living in hobo jungles.   We were horrified by the reports of the "wild children" of Russia, but they were starving little ones without parents, without any spot that they could call home.   When I was in Russia at the time, I was told that the children had heard as if from the winds and the birds of the air, certainly from no known human agency, that there was food in Moscow.   From various hamlets they met on the public roads, and when they reached Moscow they were said to number 100,000.   Our young wanderers are older.   They have homes and relatives known to them.   But though the old impulse of youth to roam must be recognized, the greater number set forth not because of lack of ties, as did the young Russians, nor of *Wanderlust,* but because of the poverty of their homes, their inability to find work in their own communities, and the futile discussions on the street corners of "what to do."

The problem of the large family with a small and irregular income is not, of course, reserved for periods of depression.   Sometimes the personality of the wage earner, sometimes the nature of his occupation, causes sharp and not infrequent ups and downs in the family fortune, and a general slump only serves to accentuate this difficulty. "Ah, yes," sighed a Scotch acquaintance, "Robbie is a grand roofer, but he's more out o' work nor in."

The resident in charge of the relief office at Henry Street reported the usual pleas varied one morning by the appearance of an Oriental-looking man who pressed for attention: "No work — no work in my trade."

"What is your occupation?"

"Lady, I am a professional mourner."

"But people die as usual."

"Yes, lady, but they do not mourn — they just bury them."

Though the mothers feel the brunt of unemployment and the real sacrifice of giving up even pennies and nickels to the children, they have a protective instinct which enables them to comprehend the price youth may pay if entirely deprived of natural outlets for fun and comradeship. In the face of dire need, it is oftentimes startling to find how deeply embedded in the mothers is the urge to save the young from hardship or from discredit with their comrades.

A mother in the last month of her pregnancy slept on the floor, that her two little children might occupy the only bed in the house. Another mother dragged home a packing box she found on the street and helped her young son make of it a chair to use at table. "He's got to learn manners," she explained. Another mother removed the outer cretonne covering from a mattress supplied her by the Red Cross, and turned it into curtains to hang at the two windows, "so home will seem nicer to my girl."

Sometimes this instinct to protect expresses itself in overindulgence that defeats efforts toward character training. I cannot forget one boy who had obtained employment in the circulation department of a New York newspaper. The office reported to the Settlement that the boy had been dishonest. He came to see me, and far into the night I tried to make him agree to take back to his employers the shoes and new suit he had bought with the money he had stolen. He fought hard. When he left me, however, I was sure that he saw the ethical point and that he would pack up the clothing and make restitution as far as was in his power. As I watched him go down the steps, thought I to myself, "I hope his grandmother [who took the place of his dead mother] does not frustrate this wholesome discipline." I was sure of the boy if she did not do so. But she did. What she said in extenuation was, "The boy is a good boy. He promised never to do it again. I did n't want him shamed."

Relief has been given in the past three years on a hitherto unknown scale, but, despite the many millions contributed by individuals, municipal, state, and national leaders realize with increasing clarity that large-scale unemployment and the relief of its victims constitute a public responsibility and one that cannot be met alone by private effort, however zealous. In our country, this necessitates a changed attitude, expressed in legislation and in new administrative machinery. We have already launched many important undertakings to this end. Perhaps it is only in time of peril and despair that we summon the courage to push ourselves forward along such new and difficult roads of social pioneering. Certainly we have had in recent experience the goad to drive us forward, however untried the way. Overwhelming need has called forth heroic response, which shows not only in the abandonment of old traditions and long-held convictions, but in a willingness to experiment with untried and even radical legislative and administrative procedure.

The public has not been left in ignorance. Admirably formulated publicity has made clear the need, and leaders in social work have detailed the methods used to meet it in reports, in interviews, in public hearings, before Congressional and legislative committees, and in statements to officials who allocate public funds. The importance of social workers gains unwonted recognition through the continuing evidence of their intelligent devotion. Walter Lippmann, that clear thinker and unimpassioned interpreter of the events of the day, said to the National Conference of Social Work (1932) : —

Among all who have had to deal with this great crisis, among statesmen and business men, among reformers and economists, your record is the clearest. You have the least to regret. You have had to administer relief on a scale which was utterly unforeseen. You have been provided with resources that were rarely adequate. The patience and the courage, the resourcefulness and the single-mindedness with which you are carrying on are beyond all praise. When the history of these times comes to be written it will be said of the social workers of America that they did their duty without flinching and that they deserved well of their country.

The army of people engaged in relief measures, working harder than it is safe for anyone to work, not only have helped shape and carry forward emergency administration, but have coördinated the various welfare agencies, knitting together the often overlapping efforts of a big city. One of the best demonstrations of this type of vital activity is in the Welfare Council of New York City, under the expert leadership of William Hodson.

Naturally the more imponderable needs have been most easily understood by those who live close to the low-waged workers of a city. Wage earners with the least margin to build up reserves of their own are also those having least assurance of the continuity of their employment. They are the first to fall by the wayside.

A man who has worked and supported his family does not take his first dismissal as a doom. He has always been on good terms with his boss and his foreman, and he feels sure that he will get work again soon. But, after an actual experience, unemployment is to him a constant threat and terror. Inadequate as it is under any scheme now put forward, unemployment insurance offers a measure of protection against this vast indignity that even in good times threatens millions of the wage earners of the Machine Age. Perhaps only such assurance of some degree of security could free from fear men like the skilled furniture finisher, whose story, though I have told it before, bears retelling, I think.

The man had had no steady work for more than two years. His wife had succeeded in getting part-time factory work. Except for the husband's occasional odd jobs, this small wage was the sole family support. One of our nurses was called in to see the wife. The diagnosis was "pregnancy complicated by underfeeding." The nurse suspected that the parents were giving to the two children most of what food they had, and were slowly starving themselves. The husband, who was over six feet tall, weighed one hundred and twenty pounds. The nurse urged the wife to give up her job and apply for aid. This the woman refused to do. "We want work. I've got to keep my job till labor pains begin." Before she returned to her home for the night, the nurse purchased the suburban papers and found to her delight a Long Island firm's advertisement for a furniture finisher. She telephoned the employer and he promised to interview the man if he came to the office at eight the next morning. That evening the nurse went back to see the anxious man, told him the good news, and gave him carfare. But the next morning she was disappointed to find him waiting at her office, already half an hour late for the possible job. "You'll never get it now!" she exclaimed. "I could n't help it," he replied dully. "After you left, my wife's pains began. I had no money to get a doctor, so I went for a policeman and he got an ambulance. The ambulance surgeon delivered her. But the baby died and he took my wife back to the hospital. I could n't leave the children or the dead

baby.   During the night I made a little coffin with some
nice wood I had.   But I don't know what to do next."
The nurse accompanied him to the morgue.   "He had
the look of Lazarus," she said.

It seems incredible that, with so much threatened
that means life and happiness, there should have been so
little organized protest.   Down in the hearts of American men and women there has been, I think, faith in
America.   Despite suffering, disappointment, and uncertainty, there has been an unshakable belief that in
time we shall find our way out.   That the revolution
we are passing through should have been so far so nearly
bloodless is due in large measure to an awakened sense
of responsibility in the community and to the knowledge
that the burden has not fallen on the wage earner alone.
As usual, there have been valorous instances of people
who have accepted the loss of much that once seemed
to them important by reappraisals of what really counts
for happiness.   And indeed the horizon is brighter, and
hope of better days is built upon sound plans which, if
carried through, will preserve the dignity and self-
respect of our people.

It was a disheartening experience, in preparing this
chapter, to go back to the report of the unemployment
committee appointed by Mayor John Purroy Mitchel,
in December 1914, of which I was a member.   On the
basis of the experience gained in that terrible winter,
the committee in its final report, submitted in 1917,
stated its conviction that unemployment is a problem
calling for constant study and attention, and for a per-

manent organization to lead the community in forestalling and mitigating its effects. The committee outlined eight major factors in a community attack on the problem: fact finding; stabilization of seasonal industries; adequate public employment service; public works planned ahead to take up the slack when private industry sags; unemployment insurance; vocational guidance and training; relief; and emergency employment. There is something almost prophetic in a sentence from the foreword to the report, written by Henry Bruère, who, as Chamberlain in the Mitchel administration, took the initiative in setting up the committee. Mr. Bruère observed, "Always industrial crises find American communities unprepared to deal with the crucial social problems which they develop."

Even as the report was submitted we began to feel the stir and lift of better times, and this valuable contribution was left to gather dust in the files. The report was reprinted and given wide circulation in 1921. But it was only in the fourth winter of the next depression that some of the recommendations of fifteen years before were embodied in legislation and in administrative machinery, notably the new state and federal relief agencies, the Wagner-Lewis public employment office measure, enacted in the 1933 special session of Congress, the provision for vast public works under the National Recovery Act, the improved gathering and dissemination of statistics of employment and unemployment under Frances Perkins, the present Secretary of Labor, who brings special training and fitness to her important post. Further, there is to be noted the steady movement toward unemployment relief through public funds rather than through private philanthropy.

Most people now realize that there is no single remedy for unemployment. There is widespread conviction that measures to correct our failures must be many and coördinated.

In addition to efforts already under way, there must be, first, security of home—and this implies housing that will meet the requirements of reasonable standards of living, on the basis of which a decent home can be built. Mothers and fathers, too, should have training for parenthood. We should make more general the far-seeing provisions for child health that have been stated and restated. Recreation suited to different ages is essentially practical, and we must not omit cultural opportunities, that life may be enriched and that all may share in the music, the drama, the libraries, the athletic contests, which have been recognized in other ages, as well as in our own, as part of the provision for right living. We need intelligent vocational guidance and training, to avoid as far as possible the round peg in the square hole, and to give a variety of skills and greater adaptability. Widows' pensions, so vigorously demanded by social workers, and established in the obligations of many states and cities, should be expanded and increased, and will be when their economy of money and childhood are more clearly understood. Old-age pensions and workmen's compensation for industrial accident and disease, so long features of European life, have entered into the American scheme of community re-

sponsibility. Unemployment insurance, now stirring
the public mind, is the logical next step toward a
measure of protection against a hazard for which the individual is not responsible and before which he is helpless. A shortened work day or work week, fortified
by minimum wage laws, will help raise the general level
of employment. Legislative standards on these matters
have matured. From the old fear of "socialism" we
have progressed to a sense of the obligation of a democracy to uphold its people.

Effort is to-day being directed toward the stabilization of industry and the elimination of cutthroat competition. There is reason to hope that the serious and
often solemn searchings of these years will in the end
prevent a recurrence of this depression experience.
The part played in the present situation by war debts,
armaments, and tariffs is recognized and strengthens
the conviction that people and problems are interrelated
the world over.

There is no one panacea to bring about a saner and
more balanced security. The intent of the people in
the settlements may seem bewildered, scattered, and, indeed, irrelevant. And yet the pressing message to which
the community is now ready to listen does have a part
in the movement toward a better-ordered society.
What is urged on the basis of knowledge and experience
has weight in furthering a reasonable provision for days
when business and industry slow down, for old age,
when life ceases to function strenuously; and preparations for right living are as essential as the stirring of

conscience which, in the last quarter of a century, has brought about our gains in the direction of widows' pensions, old-age pensions, preventive medicine, vocational guidance, the establishment of the visiting nurse to serve and to educate.   The millennium is not yet in sight, but the success that has been achieved is a challenge to every right-minded person to become interested, to study, to understand, and to participate.   Those who are despondent lest our vigilance be weakened can stiffen their courage by a backward look over the way we have come.

XI

RUSSIA AND HENRY STREET

WE have had an identification with Russia's struggle all the days of our life on the East Side. In *The House on Henry Street* I have written at some length of our introduction to the cause and its bearing upon the world as we saw it. The little revolutionary committee with which we became acquainted was mainly occupied with the rescue of political prisoners. Very few, if any, Americans had joined them; parades of mourners that marched after the news of Tsarist pogroms were entirely local. But the little group of exiles obtained in characteristic grapevine fashion information that was accurate, and the members were ready to welcome and to help any "hero" who by escape from Siberia or prison found his or her way to New York. Often we knew directly or through the committee the chapters that followed. These revolutionists had not dreamed of an economic revolution. They were united to secure freedom of assemblage, of speech, and of education for all. Escape from political despotism that was brutal and without pity absorbed them. Their private papers, if preserved, could tell the story of that period, which in resentment against the present Soviet government is often softened and sometimes forgotten.

When I was in Russia in 1924 a former maid of honor of the court, then acting as interpreter for the Quakers, sought a private interview that she might pour into my ears her tale of the unspeakable atrocities of the present government and contrast it with the fatherly protection of the old régime. Said she, "In the days of the Tsar there were no beggars in Russia." When I suggested that there were probably no beggars at the court, and described the great numbers I had seen during a visit in 1910, she insisted: "Those beggars were usually very well off. It was their trade."

A present to me from the little New York committee was a collection of photographs of men and women who had been distinguished for their sacrifices in the struggle. That gift was the expression of their faith in one who was enlisted in causes for freedom.

Marie Suklov's dramatic story was well known in this country twenty years ago. In her young life under Tsardom, acts of revolutionary violence led to a death sentence, and later, after her escape, to a sentence of exile for life in Siberia. Again she escaped, and managed to make her way to this country. While here she graduated from a training school for Montessori teachers. Now she has taken back the fruits of her years in America, and with husband and daughter is happily absorbed in teaching the oncoming generation of a free Russia. An American visitor to Russia is not surprised to identify old acquaintances from home occupied in the business of the present government, men and women from the ranks here often exhibiting ability in more responsible positions in Russia.

In Moscow in 1924 we witnessed a performance of Isadora Duncan's school. She, we were told, had been given a house and the rations allowed the "comrades"; but this was insufficient, and she was then on a tour to make more money. The house given her school was large and unattractive, as are most Russian houses I have seen. It was said to have been the home of a former favorite *ballerina* of a rich merchant. After the performance of the students, quite mediocre as measured by the performances in our Little Theatre, we were invited to say good-night to the girls. We found them in an ugly, huge bedroom with numerous mirrors and torn and spotted draperies; from the ceiling were suspended kettles of many kinds to hold the water that dripped down. Of course there was no hope that the roof which leaked so disastrously could be restored.

In a moment I felt a rush and my neck squeezed in embrace. "Oh, Neighborhood Playhouse, Neighborhood Playhouse!" cried the girl. She was one of the Duncan children who had been marooned in New York until several people came to their rescue; a visit to the Playhouse must have been a treasured memory.

Before the Revolution visitors from Russia, or those interested in the struggle, were frequent — notably the mission of Tschaikowsky, and Aladdin of unforgettable eloquence, a member of the peasant group in the Duma. In introducing them, we invited leading bankers, editors, publicists, — including the head of the Associated Press, — to listen to their impassioned plea not to lend money to the Tsarist government. After the simple Settlement dinner we gathered around the table, and the occasion developed into a conference. The visitors greatly impressed the Americans, although no programme could of course be pledged. More light was thrown on the issue when in Carnegie Hall these visitors addressed a crowded meeting in which distinguished Americans, including William Howard Taft, also took part.

Paul N. Miliukov, scholar and intrepid party leader in the Duma, came to America for one day to speak to a huge and interested audience. He took the dramatic step of this twenty-four-hour visit to New York as an effective means for gaining a wide hearing for his message. Press reports of his American address were carried by Russian papers, although direct publicity for his message was denied him in the press of his country. It is worth recording that on Miliukov's return, an opponent in the Duma spat in his face to show his resentment.

I have forgotten his public address; but Mr. Charles R. Crane, his host, arranged for a quiet luncheon, and there Miliukov appeared to be interested only in temperance propaganda and asked to have all data obtainable sent on to him, not omitting a full account of "your famous leader, Carrie Nation."

Two stalwart men in Russian blouses and high boots once called at the Settlement, and I was much moved to learn that they had been sent to us by Tolstoy. Tolstoy had died while the two friends were on their way to America. They said they came to this country in the interests of free education, meaning, as they defined it, freedom from uninteresting, rigid, traditional instruction. They had a project for a modern curriculum and modern teaching methods for Russian schools, and brought as evidence of their plan some very beautiful books for children which for safe-keeping I contributed to the library. I wanted to help them in their pilgrimage, and asked what I could do. Without hesitation they answered, "We want to meet John Dewey." That, happily, could be arranged. When I finally revisited Russia, it was to find Dr. Dewey's influence manifested in all the schools for children.

We had a meeting of rejoicing in our Little Theatre when the reins of government were entrusted to Kerenski and the end of Tsardom seemed pledged. Our government arranged an elaborate programme for the Kerenski Commission, which came to this country in July. The commission concluded its round of conference, sight-seeing, and entertainment with one unofficial visit, and that to Henry Street — made, they said, because the House was to them "a shrine that had burned for Russian freedom."

We gave no publicity to the expected visit, and confined our invitations to a reception to a very few

people who had served their cause.   But long before
our distinguished guests arrived the street before the
House was packed with Russians, many wearing blouses,
all singing revolutionary songs, tense with feeling, and
swaying as they sang.   When the members of the commission appeared, the crowd was suddenly hushed.
Then there were calls for a speech.   Bakhmeteff, head
of the commission and appointed ambassador to the
United States, climbed out of a window and, standing
on a flower box, lifted his hand for quiet.

Out of the silence, a woman's voice seemed to cut
the air: —

"Emissaries of a free Russia!" she cried.   "My father
died in Siberia.   My sister's eyes were gouged out.   I
am an exile from home.   But the price was not too great
if Russia is free!"

The *New York Times* reporter added, "The thousands
who heard her voice made her greeting their own."

Three months later came the collapse of the Kerenski
régime, and our days and nights were filled with tales of
the ruthlessness of the Bolsheviki.   But other tales
came too — of the vast promise of the Soviet government and the strength and wisdom and social passion
of Lenin.   Anna Louise Strong came back from Russia
and gave vivid pictures of the new way of life there.
She had gone into the country as a famine-relief worker
and had remained, a keen observer and skilled reporter
of incredible programmes already in motion.   She had
unusual opportunity to get information at first hand,
for she knew the leaders personally and had given
Trotsky English lessons.

At last came "Babushka," Catherine Breshkovsky, the "Little Grandmother" of the Russian Revolution, after we had heard tragic news of her and mourned her as a victim of the new régime.

Babushka telegraphed from Seattle that she would come to Henry Street, and the way the crowd mobbed her and our car as we brought her from the station was an indication of her place in New York. I had invited no one to meet her, because I feared she would be too fatigued; but in the evening many people came down to the House in the hope of seeing this great woman.

We set out the samovar and placed chairs in our largest room, and Babushka stood at one end of the room, pouring forth her hatred, her contempt for the Bolsheviki. They were murderers, traitors, unspeakably cruel; they had no interest beyond their passion for power. Her attitude was understandable, for the older revolutionists had sacrificed life and fortune, had suffered in prison, had endured exile, not for an economic revolution but to secure political and educational freedom, particularly for the peasants. Babushka was enshrined in the heart of every rebel against despotism. Her courage and strength make a Homeric tale. And when Tsardom was overthrown and she was brought back with all honor to Moscow, Kerenski was the realization of her hopes, of her vision of a free Russia. Added to this great satisfaction in a deliverance, there seemed to be a grandmotherly devotion to a beloved "boy." Brilliant Florence Kelley explained the failure of the old revolutionists to sympathize with the Bolsheviki by remarking, "They waited up all night in the station for the milk train and the express whizzed by."

While Babushka spoke a door in the far end of the long room opened and George Kennan walked in. I may remind the readers of this tale that George Kennan in his early years had been on the staff of engineers planning the first trans-Siberian railroad. On that journey into the land of exile, he met the Russian political prisoners — among them Babushka, who had been sentenced to hard labor for life in the Kara mines in the Arctic Circle. I have told how George Kennan found her, a meeting that touched the compassion of his many readers and the people who waited up all night for a chance to get into the lecture halls where he recounted the stories of these unfortunates. George Kennan and Babushka had not met since their farewell in the little Buriat village; but here he was walking into the room, an old man. Babushka paused when he reached her. "George Kennan, George Kennan!" said she, kissed him on both cheeks, and danced a little Russian dance before him.

In Babushka's Henry Street audience were two or three people who had direct communication with officials of the Soviet government. One was the wife of a man who had been superintendent of a trade school in Chicago and who had gone to Russia to help in the new society being created there. She knew of his disinterested effort on behalf of the younger generation, and she wanted to tell Babushka that there were some members of the new government who meant well and who were giving their best. For this purpose she called the next morning, but Babushka closed the door in her face. I met the visitor on the stairway, sobbing and hardly able to control her steps. She told me Babushka would not listen; then added, "But it doesn't make any difference in my feelings toward her. I was brought up to reverence her, and the sacrifices she made are no less because of her attitude now."

Babushka could not understand our willingness to listen to these destroyers of the revolution of which she and her comrades had dreamed. I venture to include here my answer to Babushka, written after her visit and in reply to her request for funds for her orphans. The programme that she offered, however, committed her American friends to an unsparing attack on the Soviet régime. The letter, I believe, expresses the reasoned views shared by many liberal Americans on a just attitude toward the Russian experiment: —

February 27, 1919

BELOVED BABUSHKA: —

I feel that I ought to write in full an explanation of my point of view, although Miss Addams and I tried when we were with you in Washington to make you see just what our position is.

Years ago when you came to America . . . we did everything that was in our power to have your voice heard and your story known; for to us you symbolized the great struggle for freedom in Russia. . . . The correspondence that your American friends have had with you during the years that followed strengthened their belief that however unpopular a cause might be, the world should know it at first hand. When the Romanov control ended in the Revolution, on that glorious March day, those of us who knew you understood what it meant to the world, and almost before we said, "Russia is free!" on our lips and from our hearts came the word, "Babushka."

Unfortunately, revolutions can never secure tranquil passage from one régime to another, and a Russian revolution had to go through the changes, strife, and civil war that must always accompany such great upheavals of the social order. Though the reports of brutalities and terroristic methods employed in Russia have shocked and grieved those Americans who do not sanction force, and who believe that democracies can never be permanent unless stable law and constitutional methods are established, nevertheless it has been borne in upon them that Russia's whole situation cannot be understood or a just attitude toward her be assumed on the partisan evidence of the conflict. For, in addition to those trusted Russians and American visitors to Russia during this critical period, who, like yourself, utterly condemn the Bolsheviki, other Americans who have had the confidence of their countrymen bring back reports that do not coincide with that sweeping condemnation.

I had understood that whatever people's views were, or whatever their position might be on the Russian political situation, they could all come together to pour money into your hands to be used for the Russian orphans, and I am eager to do my part — all of us are eager. We know exactly what your position is, and we think it could not be otherwise under the circumstances; but that is no reason why in helping you in this cause we should also become partisans in Russia's revolutionary strife and politics.

I am sure you can see that my refusal to join your committee as the invitation is presented is not from lessened love for you, but that I am standing on a principle of fairness to all people, which must guide those who venture to dedicate themselves to the cause of humanity and to democratic principles — and you yourself have been a great teacher of this.

In those world-shaking months following October 1917, the Settlement offered its hospitality to any who might interpret the purpose behind the astounding new régime. Truth seemed to be the most essential contribution that could be made to the bewildered world.

When Moissaye Olgin, the writer, — who had long resided in this country, — returned from a visit to Russia early in 1921, I have rarely seen anyone so stirred. He gave the impression of having witnessed the phenomenon of a new people risen from beneath the earth and standing up as human beings in the light of the sun. He was among the first to describe to us the method and procedure of the Soviet meetings. An audience I invited to meet him found it difficult to leave the House, so that long after a respectable time for closing the meeting they still sat enthralled and asking eager questions.

It seemed to me important that the Secretary of State, Mr. Hughes, should get this version, and not hear only of assassinations and brutality; and I arranged the interview. I have no assurance that my Russian friend made a favorable impression, and I was chagrined several days later to find he had publicly declared himself a Third Internationalist. I had expressed to Mr. Hughes my own deep assurance that this man would present the facts as would a scientist who had made a profound discovery, without prejudice or color.

Even by 1924, very few Americans had gone to Russia to see for themselves; and I gladly accepted an invitation, transmitted through Anna Louise Strong and Dr. Michael Michailovsky, — then representative of the Russian public health service in this country, — to visit Russia as guest of the government in order to discuss public health measures and problems of childhood. The party finally included Elizabeth Farrell, creator of the work for subnormal children in public schools, and Lillian Hudson, professor of nursing at Teachers College, Columbia University. We arranged to have our own interpreter, a Barnard College graduate who spoke fluent Russian. She met us in Berlin and accompanied us until we left on our trip through the Caucasus.

Our six weeks in Russia was of course a great adventure. We were entertained in the guest houses belonging to the different departments of government. We saw whatever we wanted to see, and some of the most interesting places were visited without programme or the chaperonage of our hosts. There seemed, indeed, a very general desire to have us see everything — particularly the worst in their institutions, for they were sorely troubled. I cannot say we were impressed at that time by any evidence of effective power of organization. Many of the theories of child welfare were accepted, but the practice often revealed inability to translate intellectual acquiescence into performance. However, there were many things that excited our admiration and surprise.

In a letter from Moscow, in one of those crowded

June weeks, I summed up my impression of Bolshevism
thus: —

The dictatorship is firm, strong, and harsh, and coming
from America one feels the lack of what we call democracy.
I hesitate to be critical of Russia in this respect without in-
terpreting the attitude and method of the Party in the light
of other revolutions.

Of greatest interest to us was the *Oohrana Ma-
terenstva Mladenchestva,* the division for the protection
of mothers and children, then administered by Dr.
Vera Pavlovna Lebedeva, an intelligent woman of strong
feelings and strong prejudices. We were disappointed
by their inability at that time to initiate intelligent interest in nursing and to get suitably trained nurses to
go into the rural districts. The administrator refused
to take into their training schools any women who had
belonged to the bourgeois class or to the nobility, and
many of the students accepted, we surmised, had no
habits of order and cleanliness and could not, even
with the best of formal training, fail to show their lack
of a background that included cleanly housekeeping
or even elementary laws of hygiene in the modern
sense.

Before long, Dr. Lebedeva broadened her practice on
this point. Dr. Nicholai Alexandrovich Semashko, the
Commissar of Health, who was our official host, gave this
version of the situation: "Under the old régime, none
but daughters of the aristocracy could be nurses. They
would not have tolerated anyone of less rank working
with them. Some of the aristocrats were competent

and unselfish, but with the new order the proletariat looked upon this opportunity to be nurses, freed from religious authority, as a great privilege." Doubtless Dr. Semashko had in mind the well-known nursing orders; but the hospital work was often accomplished by simple women who must have performed countless feats of labor and love.

The government officials, however, were entirely aware of the importance of giving health education to the peasants, but found their best efforts thwarted by the unwillingness of the doctors to remain in remote country regions. They were also very critical of the midwife; indeed, competent statistics, which of course were lacking, would undoubtedly have shown that Russia's infant mortality rates were the highest in any European country. The main reliance of the peasants seemed to be the *Feldcher*, an untrained person, often a barber, who did cupping, bleedings, and crude surgery. In many villages he was the only person who had any medical skill or experience.[1]

The doctors from the country districts were invited at intervals to Moscow, with all expenses paid, that they might have postgraduate study. We felt the imperative need for the well-trained public health nurse. Russian experience parallels ours in America, where the urge to be in a big city leaves few adequately trained doctors and nurses for the requirements of rural inhabitants; we advised the starting of a training school in the region of Samara, where, far from the lures of a

[1] Training courses for midwives and *Feldcher* have now been established.

big city, greater numbers might remain to serve the country districts.

After inspecting hospitals and institutions for children in Moscow, Leningrad, and surrounding communities, accompanied by one of Dr. Semashko's staff we took boat on the Volga, stopping at Kazan and at Nijni Novgorod, famous (or infamous) for the number of foundling asylums in the old days, and also for some good hospitals that had been organized under the old régime. They desired that we visit the famine region and see the pathetic, big-bellied children that were still patients in the hospitals. In these institutions we found so many assistants of one sort and another that they got in each other's way. The work was not well organized, and far too large a proportion of the available funds had to be used to feed and maintain the cumbersome personnel. Any experienced American would have been seized with a desire to bring order out of the chaos, and put what money and supplies there were to more effective use.

Before we left New York we sent to Russia a gift of movie films, pictures, charts, books, pamphlets, and other material, illustrating public health nursing in the United States, and representing an investment of several thousand dollars, as well as the expenditure of much time and care. This gift was made possible mainly through the generosity of Mrs. John D. Rockefeller, Jr., though American nurses also contributed. The exhibit was to be placed in a central library, to be loaned to such cities and rural districts as could put it to good use. The Russian forwarders had not delivered the

boxes containing the exhibit when we left, and to this
day I have no assurance that our plan was carried out.

Though we inspected hospitals and clinics and were
mainly interested in the education of nurses for the
care of the sick, we did visit many other institutions —
museums, factories to see the day nurseries for the
children of women workers, and a preventorium which
accidentally came to our attention and proved to be the
best establishment of its kind for the tuberculous that
I have seen in any country at any time. The whole
plan was adjusted to the needs of the children, and not
only provided the health measures their condition required, but was correlated with their school work as
well. The director, a Polish woman doctor who spoke
French and English with ease, referred to the institution
as a "Soviet preventorium." The type of self-govern-
ment that there prevailed we have long known in this
country in schools, camps, the George Junior Republic,
and other establishments. Nevertheless I am sure the
Russians thought they had invented the idea, and that
it was a demonstration of Communist technique.

At the time of our visit to this preventorium we
chanced upon a most interesting event. The doctor
told us that she had felt unrest and disturbance for two
days, and had then spoken to the president of the school
soviet, who had also noticed this tension. Before the
noon meal, all the boys and girls assembled in the un-
dress suitable for the tuberculous child — a loin cloth,
with a brassière added for the older girls. The president, a handsome girl of about fourteen, stood under
a tree and said: —

"Members of the soviet, I know that something is wrong. I do not know what it is. I ask for confession."

After some delay, two boys and a much more reluctant girl testified that they had been reading Fenimore Cooper's tales of Indians, and when a new company of children had arrived they had played their version of an Indian game. They had pretended to hang the newcomers, and had shot arrows at them.

The president was quite properly shocked, and asked for advice on discipline. Shouted suggestions urged that the three criminals be given the same treatment they had meted out to the newcomers.

But the doctor said, "I am your physician, and you are here for the sake of your health. It was very bad for the new members of the soviet to be subjected to this treatment. It would be equally bad for the guilty ones."

The president acquiesced, and asked for further advice.

"Put them on bread and water for a month!"

"No," said the doctor; "I cannot advise that, for the same reason I opposed the Indian punishment."

The final decision, approved by all except the three culprits, was that they should remain members of the soviet, that they should have the same food, care, and education as the others, but that they should be socially ostracized for a month. Later, at the excellent dinner, I saw these three poor creatures alone at the end of a table — speaking to no one, no one speaking to them. After the meal, when the children adjourned for games or for rest, I felt a deep sense of commiseration. The sentence was being carried out.

Since 1924 there has been much progress made by Soviet Russia in the field of public health. My account of what I observed was published in the *Survey Graphic* for December 1924. John A. Kingsbury, secretary of the Milbank Memorial Fund, who spent ample time and great care in studying the situation in the winter of 1932–1933, is enthusiastic in his report of these institutions and efforts to-day, given in *Red Medicine,* a new book of which he and Sir Arthur Newsholme are co-authors.

While in Russia we met not only the health officials but Krassin, Tchitcherin, and others of equal importance, and were greatly impressed by them. We had valuable help from the Quakers, whose house was always open to visitors, and from Nansen's agent, whose car was occasionally at our service. Nansen had been made unhappy by the insistence in many quarters that Russia's starving should be treated as political suspects rather than as helpless famine victims. Two years before our visit, he gave part of his Nobel Prize to establish in Russia large agricultural stations planned to teach peasants the use of modern farming implements.

Both music and art were shared with the young. At the opera, I saw the upper galleries filled with children from the orphanages. The museums in Russia have always been part of the educational scheme. On an earlier visit, in 1910, I had met school children with their teachers in the museums. But this was made much more important in 1924; and there were new emphases, and new museums, called "scientific" to distinguish them from the art galleries. Crowds of children filled the aisles and stood in great numbers before charts which in our country would only have interested older students. Edison's face and achievements appeared most frequently, but I took pleasure in the place occasionally given to Burbank. Henry Ford's name was often mentioned.

As I entered one famous museum a beggar sitting on the steps whispered to me, in French, not to go inside because it was "anti-Christ." When I entered I saw that one exhibit was attracting much attention. Two mummies lay side by side. One had been a sacred relic. It had been said that the form and features of a dead priest had been preserved by a miracle, and the body was believed to work remarkable cures. Where the body came from I do not know, but it was obvious that it had been skillfully embalmed. Beside the sacred relic lay an Egyptian mummy. A placard described in clear and simple terms how the human body may be preserved, even for thousands of years, by the art of the embalmer.

The schools we visited were similar in spirit to those we at home term "experimental." The educator, Stanislav T. Shatsky, an exponent of progressive methods, was called "the John Dewey of Russia," and was responsible for much of the school programme. Dr. Dewey's theory and programme had been accepted 100 per cent; but I think their application was not less than 150 per cent. At any rate, there was complete freedom to experiment. As part of the regular programme, the children stayed away from school now and then for days, or even weeks, returning with a report of what they had done for the community. We heard one boy give a very lively account of how he had rid his neighborhood of rats.

At that time Russia was trying to solve the problem of the "wild children." I shall not dwell here on the technique they were employing, since so much has been learned of child psychology since that time. But the sincerity of the workers none could question. A thousand university students patrolled the parks and streets at night to find these children and bring them to the collectors' homes. The students were given university credit for this "extra-curricular activity." I listened to a conference which a class of about fifty had with Madame Kalinin, the relative of the Soviet President — a woman worn by overwork, and probably by underfeeding, who took up each problem as a New York social worker would go over her cases with her colleagues. But in Russia at that time the child was always right; and, if he found the arrangements made for him in Moscow or in the country uncongenial, there was no pressure put upon him to remain. This has now been changed. The moving picture *Road to Life* showed the method now popular. But it seems entirely fair to say that, though new to Soviet Russia, the method has long been practised in this country for attaching a willful or perhaps antisocial lad to a wise and beloved adviser.

I found an interesting social settlement in Moscow that held many reminders of New York. But though it was unhampered, and though its conscious purpose was character development, as we use the term, rather than propaganda, its entire budget was supported by Anatole V. Lunacharsky, the Commissar of Education. His concept as an educator was broad and independent. American visitors greatly admired his attitude and looked to him for continuing guidance of Russia's tremendous educational programme. I was deeply regretful when he was displaced.   But when Eisenstein, the great film producer, was in New York not long ago, he told me he thought the removal of Lunacharsky would not in the end prove an irreparable loss to Russia. For while Lunacharsky had made all the arts — theatre, literature, ballet, music — the property of the people, he held them rigidly to their classic forms.   The present Commissar of Education allows wider experiment, he said, and may be the means of developing new forms in the arts as well as in education.

I was in Moscow when Lenin was buried in the great Red Square.   I almost expected the multitude to witness a miracle.   One saw evidences at every turn of the worship accorded Lenin.   In homes, railroad stations, offices, public buildings, his face and figure were in those places in which, on an earlier visit to Russia, I had seen sacred icons.   The thought must have penetrated my dreams; for one night as I slept I watched two spirited horses pulling a great wagon along a Russian road.   The wagon, I saw, was loaded to overflowing with crosses — rusted, bent, and broken; and when the driver turned I saw the face of Christ, radiant.

Old shrines had been torn down from their places, and some eagle emblems of the old dynasty were left contemptuously on the ground. One recalled the desecrating acts of the rabble of the French Revolution. But in Russia there was extraordinary discrimination, considering the people, the times, and the need. We visited the famous monastery situated about an hour's ride from Moscow, where the guide told us Boris Godunov lies buried. To us Boris Godunov's silver chapel was ugly, but impressive in its evident cost, with massive silver candlesticks almost reaching the ceiling. The scholarly curator unlocked doors, unlocked guarded chests, and displayed amazing treasures — jewel-encrusted vestments, and what must have been nearly priceless gold and silver goblets, also jeweled.

The sight drew the almost involuntary question, "Why were they not sold for the starving people?"

The curator was ready: "We have sold hundreds of poods of silver, gold, and jewels; but we sold nothing that had historic or artistic value." He added, "That selling was strictly carried out under the supervision of an expert sent by the authorities."

From Moscow we went by train to a mountain resort in the Caucasus famous for its mineral springs, one of which is said to have been flowing in undiminished volume since the dawn of history. Cossacks live in their villages near the splendid villas and hotels, once popular gathering places for the aristocracy. The homes and parks are now at the disposal of the new order. Where once a small, exclusive family occupied a villa and enjoyed its lawns and groves and gardens, now vacationists from factories and proletarian organizations crowd the space, enjoying their allotted holiday. We heard the tramp, tramp of files of school children, marching from the station to their quarters, when they came from the city for two weeks of "fresh air." The alert Commissar of Education had arranged for the children of special promise to remain all summer. A symphony orchestra gave concerts in the park, musicians and director wearing Russian blouses. The well-behaved audience was poorly dressed, no one in attractive clothes. Indeed "style" was nowhere apparent in Russia in 1924.

At the conclusion of our visit, we drove down the mountains to Vladikavkaz, where an automobile awaited us, and from there we traveled through the Dariel Gorge to Tiflis over the famous Georgian Military Road, finished about 1860. On one side rose great volcanic peaks, twenty of which, we were told, are higher than Mont Blanc; on the other side tumbled the roaring yellow river. We saw remnants of the tribesmen of the Caucasus, handsome, tall, and straight, and we were fortunate enough to encounter a group of the tribe who claim to be descended from the Crusaders, wearing helmets and shirts of chain mail. Strange customs persist among them, savage feuds between tribes and marriage by abduction. Women, as in ancient Oriental countries, are counted unclean when bringing forth child or during menses. We were told the "Crusaders" refuse to recognize the authority of the Soviets, and concede to current custom only in the use of silver coins; and to make certain that no God is offended, they observe three Sabbaths — Friday under the Mohammedan commandment, Saturday under the Jewish, and Sunday under the Christian.

As we neared Tiflis we were all but cremated in the terrible heat. We crawled to the floor of the car, and shaded ourselves against the sun as best we could with the robes which a few hours before had saved us from perishing with cold. We were welcomed to the hospitable quarters of the Near East Relief, where we spent some interesting days with Captain E. A. Yarrow, head of the Relief, and a mixed company of men who made their headquarters there while seeking, in the interest of banks and promoters at home, the monopoly of the manganese trade. Strange and stirring tales were told, but it was a special pleasure to the guests from Henry Street to hear enthusiastic praise of the nurses who had come from our organization in answer to the Near East call. They were working with the Armenians, and one in particular had they said, performed great deeds for the blind, the orphans, and the sick, organizing the meagre resources with unheard-of skill. The Near East established the first training school for nurses in the Caucasus, and the Armenians were received cordially and were treated as generously as the means permitted. When we saw their expulsion from Asia Minor and Turkey, and heard the tragic stories of families and individuals as we traveled on, we could not but hope they would find permanent dwelling free from persecution in the new Russia.

We left Tiflis in a private car, the gift of Queen

Victoria to the Russian Grand Duke who had been singled out for his part in the building of the road. No Soviet official would risk his good name or his political future by riding in that memento to unspeakable aristocracy; but it was turned over to the Near East Relief — really to Captain Yarrow, whom they liked and trusted. That there might be no misinterpretation, a long banner nailed to the car proclaimed the organization in possession. In the stateroom given to Elizabeth Farrell and myself we pondered on the elaborate crests on curtains and cushions; and Nikitar, the heavy-faced man who brought us tea in the early morning, must have had some emotion in his sluggish mind — for he was the selfsame servitor who had brought tea, at the same hour, to the former owners of this splendor and their guests.

We reached Batum, and again were guests of the Near East Relief, with time to discuss politics and people more freely than in Russia proper, or at the other stops we had made. But here as elsewhere we heard, almost in the same minute, tales of harsh treatment, denial of freedom, and faith in the sincerity of the dictators. On the shores of the sea were villas, with beautiful gardens and roads banked with blue hydrangeas; though the houses were poorly constructed and unattractive, the landscape as a whole suggested the Riviera.

The Italian steamer that took us across the Black Sea to Constantinople gave us poorer food and service than the Volga boat. We went slowly, and we were obliged to stop in mid-sea because the deportation of

Greeks and Armenians from Asia Minor was in progress. The children on board were forlorn, and their fare was monotonous. I obtained permission from the captain to go to the galley and bake a cake or two for them. But when I got there the cook, though friendly, gave me material entirely alien to my experience.

As I talked with him, trying to find out how to use the chunk of dry yeast and the heavy butter-substitute with which he supplied me, I asked, "Of what country are you?"

His eyes filled with tears. "All my life Austrian. Overnight they make me Italian."

In the years since the Revolution, Russia has been a subject of paramount interest. At the Foreign Policy Association, the topic brings larger crowds than any other discussion, and the famous Astor Hotel luncheons are attended to capacity whenever Russian affairs are debated. Many have been the travelers who have visited the land of the Soviets, and who, returning, have stirred interest in the subject of Russia's experiment and contributed their various points of view to our understanding, or misunderstanding, of what is being attempted and the accomplishment.

Reports from Russia are so various and often so contradictory that it is not always easy to determine where the truth lies. For years the scandal of the "nationalized women" was repeated, its basis a satire in a conservative comic paper published in Russia. I think most of us have had some experience, however, which puts us on our guard against sweeping criticism of the present régime, as well as against the ardent propagandists who see no flaw.

At a small party in Russia in 1924, an international magazine correspondent was present whom I had known slightly in New York. It was a gathering of newspaper representatives, behind closed doors, where information and opinion were freely exchanged. On this occasion most of the talk ran on the miracle of the cleanliness of new Russia — the hotels, the offices, the trains; even the boats on the Volga. (Before we left England we had been advised to take with us "a ton of Keating's insecticide" and sleeping bags, neither of which we found occasion to use.) A few weeks later, at a London dinner party, the same writer was present. This time, he was talking for his "public"; his conversation was filled with references to Russia's "foul filth," as he worded it — with details of the uncleanliness in the surroundings, and in the habits of the people. Somehow he seemed entirely forgetful of the testimony in Moscow.

Women have been sent to this country to acquire training and experience in public health nursing and to take the technique back to their own country. One nurse who came to Henry Street to obtain such experience represents the finest flower of the old aristocracy, rotten in so many places in its history. She recognizes that the indifference, the cruelty, of her class are responsible for its own extinction; and she is not alone among her people in a passionate urge to make amends. The memories of her suffering and humiliation, the terrors of prison, the hunger that gnawed, and her rescue from the noose that she had herself prepared, goad her to dedicate herself to restitution for the remaining years of her life. There will be no autobiography written by her, though her tale is almost unparalleled in the annals of the one-time great of Russia. Dignified, sure, and with sweetness of personality, she loses no opportunity to secure the best experience possible that she may be valuable to her countrymen and women. She is not a Communist. She belonged to the court circle. But she carries her sincerity plainly in her face. The Soviet leaders know that she was with Wrangel and that she threw herself against them. But they believe in her and have given her permission to leave Russia and to return to work there.

Miliukov came again to Henry Street, old and discouraged. Kerenski came. His ostensible errand was to get support for the publication put out by his anti-Soviet, but not conservative, group. Alas, Kerenski was caught between two streams! This kindly gentleman, who failed to kindle to the red heat of his country, though he gave his uttermost to the service of Russia, has seemed a pathetic victim of circumstances beyond his understanding or control.

The anthropologist, Dr. Waldemar G. Bogoras, has written the fascinating chronicle of the scientific use he and other political prisoners made of their years in the barren lands of the Bering peninsula, when they were exiles there. Back in Russia when the new government was established, he made public valuable data on the natives of the tundra and their culture. He was one of the guests at the Settlement's usual Thanksgiving dinner in 1927, and the following year we had as guest the student of anthropology for whose further work at Barnard College he had arranged during his visit to New York.

Tolstoy's daughter was our guest on Henry Street, and the officials of the Amtorg Trading Corporation have come. This organization has no diplomatic function, but is a business corporation, organized under the laws of New York, which buys and sells for clients in the Soviet Union. As an indication of what our trade with Russia might be under favorable circumstances, let me mention that in the six years ending with 1932 it had purchased about five hundred million dollars' worth of American products.

The question of the recognition of the Soviet government by the United States [2] has been discussed with no little heat, and it would be interesting to some of the most vigorous opponents to take thought of our relations with Russia in the past. Catherine the Great refused to

---

[2] The chapter on Russia and Henry Street was finished and in the hands of the publishers before the recent negotiations between Washington and Moscow began. The day those negotiations were completed, November 17, 1933, will be recorded as an eventful date in the history of the U.S.A. and U.S.S.R. Though there are doubtless individuals who hold to their prejudices and their disapprovals, to the majority in both countries the new relationship marks an achievement of justice and of wisdom. The pledges given by Litvinov on the issues that have most disturbed Americans are explicit, and go beyond those given to other Western states. In the notes and conversations, one point was stressed beyond all others: it is the evident determination of the representatives of both governments that peace shall be the dominant goal in the dealings between the United States and Soviet Russia.

acknowledge this upstart revolutionary government. To have a country without a monarch ruling by divine right or an established church seemed to her to promise a deluge from which no one could escape. It was not until 1809, thirty-three years after the Declaration of Independence, twenty years after the inauguration of George Washington as our first President, that Tsar Alexander I decided to recognize the United States of America.

The distaste for Marxism and for the fixed objective of the Soviet government to enthrone the proletariat was to be expected, and the tales of the Soviet procedures and the discipline, fantastic as many of them were, intensified prejudice in this country.

For almost a decade, inquiries to the State Department concerning recognition of Russia were referred to the "Hughes formula" — the reply of the Secretary of State in 1923 to the offer of the Soviet Foreign Minister to discuss all matters at issue between the two countries. Mr. Hughes held that no negotiations were needed, since the chief points at issue as he defined them — the repudiated Russian debts, compensation for confiscated American property, and cessation of Moscow's Communist propaganda in this country — could be settled by Russia without conference with us. Under the present Administration, nothing has been heard of the "Hughes formula." The whole situation between the two countries is now modified by the fact that Soviet Russia is no longer unique in failing to meet her obligations to us, since so many European governments have become our defaulting debtors.

IN NATIVE COSTUME

There are certain points, important in themselves but perhaps not of diplomatic measure, that ought, in my opinion, to be taken into account. They seem to me to constitute very practical reasons why recognition should not longer be deferred.

Whether or not one agrees with its principles, the present government has been sustained against terrific odds for more than fifteen years. There is no other government in the world that has done as well. Presidents, prime ministers, have disappeared; parties have been extinguished or have sprung into sudden power; kings and queens have been exiled; bases of currency have shifted; constitutions have been abrogated; techniques of diplomacy revolutionized. By our steadfast refusal to recognize this government that has so dramatically shown its stability, our markets have been deflected at a time when the wealth of the country seems to melt away. With the wheels of American industry stalled because of the slack in our trade, we have not been able to take advantage of this potentially great market, and we have seen a source of income and employment diverted to other countries. Such trading as has been carried on between Russia and certain American concerns has been handicapped greatly because we have no official representatives in Russia, and difficulties have to be referred to the representatives of other countries. Without touching upon the political significance, it seems to me unthinkable that where there is so much in common, so many interests and aspirations, we should continue the present awkward relationship by refusing to acknowledge formally the obvious fact of a responsible government in Russia.

The question has often been debated as to whether recognition means approval. It is, of course, a matter of practical convenience; and in regard to Russia, as to other governments, approbation is not implied. And there is abundant evidence of the change in emphasis of the Soviet government from propaganda abroad to effort at home. Walter Duranty, famous Moscow correspondent for the *New York Times*, quotes the amazement of an American visitor who compared May Day, 1918, — the first after the Bolshevik revolution, — with May Day, 1933: —

That first May Day all the stress of the speeches and slogans was on world revolution — "Workers, throw off your chains!" "Soldiers, leave your trenches!" "Peasants, seize your land!" "All together for world revolution and proletarian brotherhood!"

This year there was not one word of international revolution — everything was national. But by national I don't mean nationalist. In 1918 they thought in terms of world revolution; in 1933, in terms of their own effort.

The farseeing diplomacy of Litvinov, the present Commissar for Foreign Affairs, gives assurance that this attitude will be maintained. Edwin L. James, reporting the Economic Conference in London, comments on this point: —

As a matter of fact, the Third International has much diminished its efforts to bring about a world revolution, and its activities in this as well as other countries have decreased in recent years. One may count upon Litvinov to try to keep these efforts at a low ebb, for they have always been a hindrance to his activities.

Recognition seems to me not only a matter of justice and practical expediency, but a step of vital importance in our hope for better understanding and coöperation between the nations of the world. For, internationally as well as nationally, it is a basic fact that you cannot build up any social structure on hatred and suspicion.

XII

TOWARD PEACE

THIS chapter is not written as history, but rather as a chronicle of events which illustrate the influence of small minorities in affairs of far-reaching public interest. As I look back, it seems to me that our efforts toward peace, even in the midst of war, bulk large in the story I have set myself to tell; they show, I think, that a small group having profound and selfless interest in the going world is not useless, and its position and its influence may without embarrassing publicity contribute to the clarification of problems of the day.

The Settlement was of course shaken by the shot that brought war upon the world. The night after war was declared my telephone rang, and the voice of a woman of the press explained that she, and her colleagues who were with her, felt that there should be

immediate protest on the part of the women of America.
They thought of a parade, and pledged their help in the
preliminary organization.   Would I head it?   I agreed
at once — with the proviso that Mrs. Henry Villard,
the daughter of Garrison, should lead the line; I would
walk behind her.

Quickly the plans too. shape.   In less than two
weeks, New York saw a st'rring expression of the resistance of women to war.   The *New York Herald* of
August 30, 1914, began its 'ong, illustrated account
thus: —

Twelve hundred women, sisters in protest against the
horrors of war, walked yesterday in Fifth Avenue between
walls of silent spectators to the bea' of muffled drums.
Many were in deepest black, others were in white with ribbons
of sable hue on their sleeves, a few still wo·e the bright colors
of summer touched with badge of mourning.

The solemn sympathy of the massed spectators was
evidently caught by the reporter, who further wrote: —

In reverent silence the crowd which lined Fifth Avenue
from Fifty-Seventh to Seventeenth Streets greeted the marching women.   Applause would have been manifestly inap-
propriate.   Windows of the big hotels and business houses
each framed their quota of solemn, approving faces.   There
were a few instances where the feelings of the spectators gave
vent to hand clapping and cheering, but generally the thousands who lined the route seemed to feel that applause was
not in keeping with the solemnity of the occasion and an
intense hush prevailed, broken only by the reverberating,
dirge-like roll of the muffled drums.

The *New York Times* commented editorially: —

It was a concrete expression of the feelings and the profound interests, as to war, of that vast element in the community, the women, who suffer most from war's evils and have least to say or to do regarding entrance on war.

It is tragic to remember how soon the natural resentment to war by women, formulated long ago in *The Trojan Women*, was dissipated by the clamor of the patrioteers, and how their treasured spiritual and reasoning convictions were made objects of dislike, and sometimes of persecution.   There appeared in time the Lusk reports, in which many of our colleagues were held up to scorn; these were followed by the famous "spider web," and the D.A.R. "black list."

Much of this opposition was underground, but many individuals retained the outspoken love and loyalty of those who differed with them.   Some there were who disagreed with us, yet looked upon Jane Addams and John Lovejoy Elliott and others of our company with sorrowing pity rather than with scorn.   I presume that Miss Addams came in for the most violent attacks, because she was our incomparable leader.   But long before this country entered the War the changing attitude was manifested in increasing volume.

War fever is a virulent disease, and people fired by propaganda may do things and say things foreign alike to character and to principles.   In the winter of 1913, when there were no rumors of war here, I found myself seated at a dinner party one evening next to Professor Josef Redlich, now of the Harvard Law School, at that time best known as one of the leaders of the Austrian parliament and considered an authority on the Balkan situation. The conversation turned to politics, and Redlich said: "Austria is mobilized for war with Russia; but the Emperor hopes he will not have to live through another war, and there is deference to his wishes." In spite of the well-known programme of his group, Redlich added that he had said in parliament that he would be willing to support war against Tsarist Russia.

I thought it worth while to repeat this to my friend Jacob H. Schiff, whose opposition to Russia, because of the persecution of the Jews, would give him a special interest in such a statement. Said Mr. Schiff, "Austria will have to demobilize. And I would do anything I could, should the situation arise, to prevent a loan to Austria for other than constructive purposes. For if war started there, all Europe would be aflame. I fear England might be drawn into it, and it is within the realm of possibility that this country might become involved." I learned later that a loan to Austria, then under consideration, was not made, probably due to Mr. Schiff's convictions; but there seems to be no way to prevent war, once diplomacy influences the minds of a people to turn that way. Social workers are not likely to be silent when danger menaces the good will of peoples toward each other. Theirs is a passionate desire to guard against disharmonies and to encourage people to know one another and to comprehend what they are and what they know.

Less than a month after the first declaration of war,

Jane Addams and Paul Kellogg, then as now the brilliant editor of the *Survey,* joined me in calling together
eighteen or twenty social thinkers — recognized community leaders — at Henry Street.   We stated our purpose in convening them thus: —

We suppose that never before has society been self-con-
scious enough carefully to note the subtle reactions of war,
inevitably disastrous to the humane instincts which had been
asserting themselves in the social order.   We feel that, whatever the fortunes of the conflict, we are concerned that certain things in the civilization of Europe and in each of the
warring countries shall not perish.

While the United States must as a noncombatant nation
maintain a neutral attitude, so much is at stake in both war
and reconstruction that on the day when, as President Wilson
has said, the nations of Europe come together for settlement,
Americans should, as freemen and democrats and peace lovers,
express themselves in some affirmative way.

This round table is suggested as a means by which in
humbleness and quiet some of us who deal with the social
fabric may come together to clarify our minds and, if it
seems wise, to act in concert.

As I write I have before me the minutes of that meeting, and something of the confusion and uncertainty of
that day comes back to me: our horror of war, our
sanguine belief that nothing so dreadful as the European
conflict could long continue, our passionate desire to
further any effort toward an early and a lasting peace.

After our all-day deliberations we voted "to draft a
statement which, like that of a group of British authors,
would voice the feeling of social workers in America";

and an informal committee, of which I served as chairman, was organized for the purpose.

It is not necessary to detail the process here step by step; but gradually there grew up a compact organization to serve as the spearhead for efforts toward a lasting peace, and to exert influence against militarism and on the side of civilized relationships between nations. Thus I presently found myself chairman, not of an informal committee, but of the American Union Against Militarism, which had evolved from that first groping conference on Henry Street.

American policies toward the holocaust in Europe were of course our fundamental concern; but for the first two years a situation closer home repeatedly claimed our attention — the menace of a war between the United States and Mexico.

We were damned by some for our part in keeping the United States out of that war. Our group activity is to me memorable, not because of the part it played at that tense moment of history, but because it furnished an example of the round-table conference as a substitute for war.

Recent as are the events, very few people seem to remember the facts; and only a historian now and then speaks of our long-time misbehavior toward our neighbor republic. There is a wealth of literature on the subject; this is not the place to review our occasional good intentions and our frequent exploitation, nor to recall how steadily burned the camp fires in the minds of many of the people. Our group, — small in numbers but strong in convictions, — watching the signs of the day, saw the menace on the Border. The occupation of Vera Cruz was inflammatory; but after it the peril seemed to subside. That this occupation was a blunder was hardly contradicted even by the most devoted friends of the Administration. So, too, was the doubtless well-intentioned refusal to "take the bloody hand of Huerta." Then came Villa's raid across the Border, with the heartless loss of life and property in a little New Mexican town, promptly followed by Pershing's pursuit of the bandits, undertaken with Carranza's reluctant consent.

The boiling point was reached with what to-day's histories call "the Carrizal incident." Then, it was "the Battle of Carrizal." For two hours two troops of colored American cavalry, trying to pass through the little Mexican town El Carrizal, fought against a superior Mexican force that barred their way. Across the front page of the sober *New York Times,* the morning of June 22, 1916, the headlines screamed: —

AMERICAN CAVALRY AMBUSHED BY CARRANZA TROOPS
SCORES, INCLUDING MEXICAN GENERAL, REPORTED SLAIN
PERSHING SHIFTS ARMY; WASHINGTON EXPECTS BREAK

The stories that followed accentuated rather than minimized the headlines.

With the world at such tension, this interpretation of the episode to the American people — as an unprovoked attack by troops of the regular Mexican army — inevitably meant war. Fortunately, there was immediately available an official statement from an American officer, Captain Morey, written at the scene of the conflict.   As he lay wounded near the battlefield, not expecting to reach the Border alive, Captain Morey reported: —

CARRIZAL, MEXICO
June 21, 1916, 9.15 A.M.

To the Commanding Officer, Ojo Frederico: My troop reached Ojo Santo Domingo at 5.30 P.M., June 20.   Met C Troop under Captain Boyd.   I came under Captain Boyd's command and marched my troop in rear for Carrizal at 4.15 A.M., reaching open field to southeast of town at 6.30 A.M.

Captain Boyd sent in a note requesting permission to pass through the town.   This was refused.   States we could go to the north, but not east.   Captain Boyd said he was going to Ahumada at this time.

He was talking with Carranza commander.   General Gomez sent a written message that Captain Boyd was bringing force in town and have a conference, Captain Boyd feared an ambush.   He was under the impression that the Mexicans would run as soon as we fired.

We formed for attack, his intention being to move up to the line of about 120 Mexicans on the edge of the town. . . .

When we were within 300 yards the Mexicans opened fire, and a strong one, before we fired a shot; then we opened up. They did not run. . . .

I am hiding in a hole 2000 yards from field and have one wounded man and three men with me.

(Signed)   MOREY, *Captain*

Here was evidence to show that the clash occurred after the Americans had been refused permission to pass through the town, and that the Mexicans had

fired only when our troops advanced in battle forma-
tion. This clearly was a situation very different from
the "ambush" and "unprovoked attack" of the front
pages, and a declaration of war could hardly be based
on the occurrence if the public knew the facts.

Amos Pinchot, lawyer and alert citizen, who had
from the beginning been active in our Union, telephoned early in the morning, filled with apprehension
lest the headlines would be acted upon as a call to
battle unless the Captain's report were given wide publicity at once. There was a possibility, under the influence that might prevail, that the report would be
suppressed. Our executive committee met that evening at the home of Alice Lewisohn, a member of the
Union, and arranged by telephone and telegraph to have
Captain Morey's statement carried as a display advertisement in leading dailies. Roy Howard, now president and editor in chief of the Scripps-Howard Newspapers, helped us plan this publicity. The press was
generous in terms, and several papers on the Border,
where the heat was dangerous, copied these four-column
advertisements without charge. Here, when it was
most needed, was far-flung and convincing information
that was a bulwark against war with Mexico.

Less conspicuous but even more memorable than the
broadcast of Captain Morey's report was the experiment with the technique of friendly conference on
which we almost simultaneously embarked.

The fact that the American Union Against Militarism sent David Starr Jordan, President of Leland
Stanford University, to the Border as chairman of an

unofficial American-Mexican Committee may seem to some an insignificant matter. Paul Kellogg, who happened to be in the Middle West at the time, reading the front page which flamed with war incitement, found only one evidence of a calmer opinion. That one evidence was a brief paragraph announcing Dr. Jordan's arrival in Texas. There were threats on the Border of tarring and feathering him. But this courageous leader had been a beloved teacher as well as a peace advocate, and some of his former students were living in the community, one of them an influential banker. They organized, quietly but very effectively, to protect him and also the good name of the city of El Paso. Dr. Jordan himself was wholly indifferent to the threats. The committee finally came together in Washington instead of in El Paso. It would have been impossible for men to talk quietly and constructively in the feverish atmosphere of the Border.

This overture by a small group of private citizens seemed one sane note in those hysterical days. Though there is little in the way of practical result to show for their deliberations, they did demonstrate that Americans and Mexicans could get together and talk things over. The whole experiment afforded a sample of reasonable action, and prepared the ground for the official commission later organized by the two governments.

Though the threat of immediate war receded, the situation remained tense as the sultry summer of 1916 dragged on. Pershing was still in Mexico, with his troops stretched along a four-hundred-mile line; and our newly confirmed ambassador, Henry P. Fletcher, had not been sent to his post. Early in September, the President appointed Secretary Lane, Judge George Gray of Wilmington, Delaware, and John R. Mott of the International Y.M.C.A. the American members of an official American-Mexican Commission. Dr. L. S. Rowe of the Pan-American Union served as secretary. Their instructions were simply "to see what could be done."

During the preliminary work of the official group, we of the American Union Against Militarism did what was possible to keep the public reminded that the Mexican people are not roughnecks, ignorant Indians — nor altogether alien to our own principles and practices. We met the Mexican members of the commission socially in New York, and found them very sympathetic. One was a lover of Tagore. It was hard for him to keep to politics — he wanted to talk poetry. We had a party at the House on Henry Street in honor of these official visitors. Other friends entertained them. But there still was a conviction that Mexicans were "not like us" — which we all know means not simply different, but inferior. We frequently discussed with the Mexican representatives our belief that their countrymen were missing a great opportunity in not bringing into the United States their singers, their dancers, their artists, their achievements as cultivated people. Americans were "fed up" with bandits.

During the commission's deliberations David Lawrence, then correspondent for the *New York Evening Post,* wrote disturbing reports about conditions in Mexico. It is a pleasure to record here that a long-distance telephone message to Mr. Lawrence that his accounts did not tally with our information brought him that evening from Washington to New York. He offered to leave by the night train for Mexico to get the most accurate information available. The notable series of twelve articles that he wrote as a result of that trip did much to enlighten the American public on the situation in Mexico, and to fix our responsibility and our opportunity to establish sound relations with our neighbor to the south.

One noon, while I was at luncheon, a telephone call came from Secretary Lane in Washington, asking me to come on to meet with the American members of the joint commission. Paul Kellogg and I, with only an hour and a half to clear up our busy desks and catch the train, got aboard the Congressional Limited that January afternoon. Our train was late in arriving; at the gate we found Henry Bruère, then with the American Metals and Mining Company. He was one American business man who had not only factual information but real understanding of Mexican affairs. He had been summoned because of his knowledge of Mexican mining and his known insight and fairness. We went together to Secretary Lane's house, where we found the American members of the commission. They were in great distress because they were making no headway. For many weeks they had forgathered with the Mexicans every day, and had pleasant intercourse; but nothing happened. They felt stalemated. More especially, they felt very uncertain as to whether they could obtain the backing of the American public for conciliatory and constructive action. The interest and stand taken by our group seemed to offer evidence of reserves of public opinion that were reassuring to them, and, almost in despair, they had reached out for help. I was in conference with them until long after midnight. Before I left Washington next morning, at Secretary Lane's request I dictated a letter covering the suggestions we had made informally the evening before. Dr. Rowe wrote that this contribution "threw light into a darkened room." The contribution seems worth quoting here, in part: —

We believe that the presence of the army throws emphasis upon our military relations, and coupled with the fact that our ambassador is absent from his post must give to the Mexicans, as it does to others, an impression that we are an enemy country. If we were frankly at war with Mexico what further steps could we take than to keep an army on their soil and withdraw, or to all intents and purposes withdraw, our civil representative? Cannot the statement be made that the army, having accomplished its original purpose and having been sent to Mexico in the belief that it would be of help to Carranza, is now withdrawn because its continued presence seems to be a disadvantage to the government that we wish to help and that we recognize? If vigor could be injected into the statement, that would place clearly before the Mexicans and before those Americans who are watching and who are really interested the affirmative, constructive suggestions for the upbuilding of Mexican social and economic life, would we not be placed before the Mexicans and the others in exactly the right light! The statement that the army would leave because its presence is no longer valuable would take its unimportant position as compared with the sincere, thoughtful programme that we would be willing to carry out if the Mexicans through their first chief so desired. . . .

It seems to me, Mr. Secretary, if you and your colleagues could make this the occasion of a magnanimous statement (one that you could so well formulate) concerning our relations to Mexico, that you would not only be contributing greatly to Mexico and to America, but that it would be a demonstration to the whole world of the possibility of carrying out through negotiations vexed problems that arise between nations. With our President standing before the warring countries as one who urges the practicability of so settling troubles between neighboring nations, it seems to me that the occasion is great and your opportunity great.

That advertisement of the Carrizal incident proved an effective measure. It could have been taken only by an independent group, informed and able to act quickly. The opinion then and later prevailed that without it the report of the Captain might have been lost in the files and the country would have been keyed to war pitch by the belief that Mexicans had treacherously ambushed American troops. Again it was not the diplomats or the militarists, but rather a little group of private citizens, who proved that in the midst of such tension Americans and Mexicans could sit down together to discuss the issues.

To-day great changes have come about, and President Roosevelt and his associates have laid their hands to the implements offered a decade ago in dealing with Mexico and warring Europe: conference and understanding instead of armies. One likes to recall that the different groups who have had faith in this method have helped bring about new thought and informed action.

No one, I believe, who played a public part in the War period can look back to those years without a keen awareness of Woodrow Wilson as the pivot on which history then turned. His idealism, his magic with words, his aloofness and severity, the strange conflicts within his spirit, the triumph of his personality and its defeat, are bound up with any attempt to recall and to interpret events between 1914 and 1918.

I had a slight acquaintance and likewise some correspondence with him before he became President. After his election, but before his inauguration, Mrs. Caroline B. Wittpenn, widely known for her great work in prison reform, invited a company of social workers to meet Mr. Wilson at a Sunday afternoon tea at her home in Hoboken. She told us that she "wanted to give him opportunity to know the minds of social workers." But Mr. Wilson was formal in meeting the company. He did not enter into any discussion of the experience and outlook of the interests represented, nor did he ask questions or make comments that would lead to understanding. He seemed to know superbly how to state opinions, but not how to elicit information from others.

The next day, by chance, I spent several hours with Theodore Roosevelt. He was much concerned over a strike in our neighborhood, and asked me to lunch with the staff of the *Outlook*. It was a jolly occasion, with joking and much laughter and exchange of stories. But

Theodore Roosevelt wanted to know about that strike: not only the issues and the possible terms of settlement, but about the individual workers — even the names of the girls. He knew how to draw one out, how to get at all the human interests in the dispute.

At the Residents' Meeting next evening there was great interest because I had seen the President-elect and the ex-President within the few hours. My colleagues wanted impressions. I could best summarize mine by stating that while I was sure Woodrow Wilson would never learn from folks, I was equally sure that Theodore Roosevelt had seldom sought his wisdom in books. He felt instinctively that it is the sense of people and of life that gives significance to facts of history and economics and government.

It came about that there were many occurrences that took me to the White House during the War period, usually at the President's invitation. Although these visits were sometimes in order to register a protest, Mr. Wilson's courtesy was unfailing.

Woodrow Wilson was a connoisseur of good stories. He was not afraid of slang: I am told he was not afraid of "cuss words." No one could enjoy more than he the full flavor of a Henry Street story his wife passed on to him near the end of his days. A great parade had marched up Fifth Avenue, which the President reviewed. Three nurses, of whom I was one, led that section of the line. But something went wrong with the order of the march. We couldn't get a marshal all through the day. The band seemed always half a mile ahead of us, the column of nurses half a mile behind. We three felt very foolish as we passed the reviewing stand, very conscious of the blanks before and behind us. That evening, one of the Settlement's neighbors called upon us. He was a local character much exploited by the newspaper men, who often took him along to public spectacles for the sake of the pungent comments with which to "color" their stories. That evening he was very proud. He had attended the parade with the press, and had had a place of vantage. He asked me what I thought of it. Still somewhat exasperated by our experience, I said I thought it was the worst parade in which I had ever marched. His face fell.

"Well, the President did n't feel that way," he said. "I was right next him. And he kep' sayin', 'most every minute, 'My Gawd, ain't that some parade!' "

One of my friends had recently returned from England with new ideals of diction, and corrected my pronunciation of "stabilize." She insisted that the first syllable should rhyme with "cab." Knowing that the President was a purist in the spoken word, I asked Mrs. Wilson to refer the point for arbitration. In a few days there came a note of thanks for the parade story. Mr. Wilson added, "There is no basis whatever for any pronunciation except 'stable.' But here is another instance that the English cannot learn to speak our language."

Several of my associates in the American Union Against Militarism and I had a revealing and, I have thought, significant interview with President Wilson in the troubled spring of 1916, not long before the

Mexican situation came to a head. We had viewed with uneasiness the President's sudden shift to a strong preparedness position, and his apparently successful effort to take the country with him. Soon after the Christmas holidays, he made his famous "swing around the circle" to put before the Middle West the case for a greatly strengthened army and navy. In the course of a speech he gave in St. Louis, which concluded the trip, he urged, ironically, that those who disagreed with him "hire large halls" and state their views.

Our group took President Wilson's suggestion literally, and hired the largest halls obtainable in eleven leading cities. At Carnegie Hall in New York, under a banner proclaiming "Democracy Versus Militarism," we launched our effort to put before the country "the truth about preparedness."

On that occasion I summarized our position thus: —

Under the seemingly reasonable term "preparedness," militarism has invaded us from every side, and even marched into our schools, threatening by legislative enactment where exhortation failed to establish conscription there. Extraordinary and unprecedented measures have been taken to promote a public demand for military and naval expansion, and these have brought in their train hysteria and the camp followers of self-interest.

More than forty thousand persons attended these anti-militarism mass meetings, and the message of our speakers obtained much wider hearing through the press. At the end of our "swing around the circle," a memorial was presented to the President, reporting the anti-militarist spirit in the country as our speakers had been made aware of it. On May 8 this summary of opinion was carried to the White House by a small delegation. The group spent an hour with the President, in an interview to which Mr. Wilson had invited the press. My own memory has been refreshed by referring to the front-page account of the conversation carried by the *New York Times* the following day. Mr. Wilson opened the discussion by expressing his fundamental disagreement with the consideration we put before him.

The *Times* quotes me thus: "There is an effort to stampede the country into militarism."

"But it is not working," the President retorted. He went on to discriminate between "reasonable preparation" and "militarism." "I am just as much opposed to militarism as any man living," he said; "I think it is a deadly thing to get into the spirit of a nation."

He made a further distinction between "universal military service" and "universal military training"; but stated that even in regard to the former his mind was still "to let."

In suggesting the need for stronger national defenses he put forward for the first time, so far as I know, his idea of "a family of nations." If such a league were to be able to say, "You shall not go to war," he submitted, there would have to be some sort of international military force "to make that 'shall' bite." He added, "And the rest of the world, if America takes part in this thing, will have the right to expect from her that she contribute her element of force to the general understanding."

I asked whether this might not logically lead to "a limitless expansion of America's contribution." He replied: —

"Well, logically, Miss Wald; but I have not the least regard for logic. What I mean to say is, I think in such affairs as we are now discussing the circumstances are the logic." And he concluded, "Now, quite opposite to anything you fear, I believe that if the world ever comes to combine its force for the purpose of maintaining peace, the individual contributions of each nation will be much less, necessarily, than they would be in other circumstances; and that all they will have to do will be to contribute moderately, and not indefinitely."

But, in spite of the President's vision of international coöperation and the pacifist campaign slogan that was so large a factor in Woodrow Wilson's reëlection, the country was hurtling toward war. In February 1917 Germany announced the resumption of unrestricted submarine warfare, and a few days later we broke off diplomatic relations. Through our group the possibility of employing the policy of "armed neutrality" resorted to by the United States a century before, during the Napoleonic conflicts, was put before the President as a measure short of war which might conserve our position as a neutral and give him the chance to act in line with his recent declarations for a "peace without victory." The move was attacked in the Senate as a stepping-stone to war, and Wilson resented this sharply.

"Armed neutrality" was, as the event proved, a measure that might lead either way. As the country embarked upon its brief experiment with this policy, Pershing's force was finally withdrawn from Mexico. A few weeks later we had joined the Allies.

The reaction of our neighbors on Henry Street to the fact of war was for a long time sheer bewilderment. Many of them had come from backward and oppressed countries, where compulsory service was a tragedy in their lives, to seek the greater opportunity offered by a free land. They had not dreamed that a great, modern, intelligent nation could become involved in war. War could not be an enthusiasm with them, and they were slow to kindle.

There was grieving in the homes of the neighborhood when the Selective Service Act went into effect, but by that time the young men had been stirred by war propaganda. They wanted to go. We turned over one of our houses to the local draft board. Our boys' worker was released from his duties, with his salary continued, that he might serve as chairman of the board. We wanted the machinery administered under the best conditions, and this arrangement made it possible for the boys to come to a place they knew was friendly and to an agent they knew was sympathetic. There was no harshness in the way the provisions of the draft went into effect on Henry Street, and there was subsequently great pride in the majors and captains and lieutenants from our ranks.

The Settlement was the scene of hurried weddings as the boys were called into service, and we were left to look after young wives and old mothers. The House made every effort to mitigate the sufferings of war. Though their load of work increased, our nurses took part in the parades; and there were always cheers and bouquets for the blue-clad women as we marched with the Red Cross. We carried no war standards. We were conservers of life.

Even before the United States entered the War we felt, as did so many other educational groups, the first touch of the heavy hand of censorship and repression. In July 1916 our Little Theatre staged *Black 'Ell*, an anti-war play by Miles Malleson. Colonel House and a member of the Cabinet were dinner guests at the Settlement, and later in the evening we went to the play. These gentlemen and their wives spoke warmly about the performance. The play had attracted the attention of pro-militarists; that same evening a group, probably sent to pass judgment, left the theatre with ostentatious disapproval. There was to be only one more performance, but the next morning we received word that the play must not go on. Mayor Mitchel was in Albany at the time, and I discussed the matter with Arthur Woods, then Commissioner of Police. The Commissioner of Licenses had mandated the order. I told Colonel Woods that if the performance were forbidden, the audience would be permitted to assemble and then I, from the stage, would tell them why the curtain could not rise. It was decided to let the play continue.

Another incident marked that particular evening. As I left the theatre one of our boys, with a word of apology for taking my attention from my guests, said,

"I know how you feel about armies; but I do not feel that way. I want to enlist. Do you mind?" Needless to say, my reply was, "Of course not!" I added, "Follow your own convictions. Nothing should hold you back from doing what you think is right."

When our neutrality ended and preparations for our active participation in the War absorbed the energy and attention of the country, the divergent attitudes of the participants in the Union's activities did not simplify an essentially difficult situation. Some were free lances, while others carried weighty responsibilities. The Union, as an instrument of minority opinion, was needed at that time; but its period of usefulness was shortened by these differences. Brilliant and courageous were the members of the staff, but temperamentally ready to advocate the most extreme measures — sometimes because they were the most extreme. Contrariwise, a measure that was not radical, that failed to meet their eager urge for action, was thereby likely to be considered wrong and antisocial. But maturer experience sanctions patience till the right moment for action. Many decisions based upon careful and truly courageous considerations and a passionate desire for righteous achievement need the slower processes of conference, and of elucidation of disputed points. There is a valid distinction between the two patterns. Of course this does not overlook the obligation to be ready to sacrifice one's most precious possession where and when the challenge comes to stand by a principle of conduct or to meet a crisis.

It is not easy to appraise the relative efforts to enhance the security of life and living. In striving for peace and good will among all peoples one had to risk, in War days, condemnation by those who disapproved of a patriotism outside their definition of the true meaning of the word. Though we had unnumbered evidences from people and from the press of the esteem in which the Settlement, and particularly the Nursing Service, were held, there were heartbreaking punishments meted out to me because of my pacifist principles. I was disciplined by the torture-chamber method of having the money withdrawn which enabled the nurses to care for the families of the soldiers no less than the other sick. It is useless to detail the considerations that upheld me in difficult days — the veritable clamor of the frightened people for the nurse, the knowledge that sympathetic opinions were current though not always expressed, the fact that many of our staff were absent overseas, the knowledge that we were continually asked to interpret rulings to the people who might otherwise have demonstrated resentment, and that the settlements were a kind of insurance against leaderless hotheads. There was no criticism of the values of the services given. There were, at the same time, frequent gifts and the splendid understanding of people who, while declaring their difference in opinion, expressed with emphasis their support of those of us who were unafraid to give voice to convictions.

From the moment of our entrance into the War, the American Union Against Militarism worked not only for early and lasting peace, but for the preservation of traditional American liberties. A week after the decla-

ration, twenty of my colleagues joined me in signing
a letter to President Wilson, expressing our concern
"lest America, having declared a state of war, should
sacrifice certain safeguards fundamental to the life of
her democracy." We gave our strongest support to
legislation pending or being framed "seeking to punish
those who designedly use military information for the
benefit of foreign governments"; but we pointed out:

Even by this time, we have seen evidence of the breaking
down of immemorial rights and privileges. Halls have been
refused for public discussion; meetings have been broken up;
speakers have been arrested and censorship exercised, not to
prevent the transmission of information to enemy countries
but to prevent the free discussion by American citizens of
our own programmes and policies.

What we ask of you, Mr. President, whose utterances at
this time must command the earnest attention of the country, is to make an impressive statement that will reach, not
only the officials of the federal government scattered throughout the Union, but the officials of the several states and of
the cities, towns, and villages of the country, reminding
them of the peculiar obligation devolving upon all Americans in this War to uphold in every way our constitutional
rights and liberties. This will give assurance that in attempt-
ing to administer war-time laws the spirit of democracy will
not be broken. Such a statement sent throughout the country would reënforce your declaration that this is a war for
democracy and liberty. It is only because this matter seems
of paramount public importance that we venture to bring
it to you at this time for your attention.

In reply the President wrote: —

DEAR MISS WALD: —

The letter signed by yourself and others under date of April sixteenth has, of course, chimed in with my own feelings and sentiments. I do not know what steps it will be practicable to take in the immediate future to safeguard the things which I agree with you in thinking ought in any circumstances to be safeguarded, but you may be sure I will have the matter in mind and will act, I hope, at the right time in the spirit of your suggestion.

Cordially and sincerely yours,
WOODROW WILSON

A ringing statement in defense of civil liberties was not made; but with the President's permission the correspondence was given to the press, and in that way the point of view expressed in our letter, and concurred in by Mr. Wilson, was put before the public — not, of course, with the effectiveness of a White House message on the subject.

As the War went on, differences of outlook within the American Union Against Militarism divided the executive committee into three groups. There were the ardent, head-on anti-militarists; there was the group primarily interested in civil liberties, some of them going so far as resistance to the draft; the third group, the one with which I was in harmony, was chiefly concerned with finding alternatives to war.

From 1914 to 1917, the year of our entrance into the War, the American Union Against Militarism met the situations as they arose, according to its conception of responsibility and patriotism. The members of the staff and of the executive committee were deeply involved. They poured out all the force of their ardent faiths in their efforts on behalf of peace; and their endeavor reflected, in spite of their differences, a spirited collaboration. The fire and imagination of the Secretary, Crystal Eastman, were often impatient of more sober councils; looking back upon that anxious time, it seems to me that a fusing of judgment, statesmancraft, and human warmth kept our eyes steadily on the goal and our feet on the ground.

Finally, feeling that my effort to hold together so divided an organization was no longer justified, in the summer of 1917 I resigned as chairman of the Union. Out of the group's diversity of interest grew the American Civil Liberties Union, which to-day does such intrepid work under Roger Baldwin's leadership, and the Foreign Policy Association, which not only provokes interest in international affairs but is also an educational influence on the side of statesmanlike and farseeing national policy.

Many social workers and students of public affairs felt the need of a liberal effort (pro-war as well as pacifist) to work out a programme for a democratic peace. Nineteen ardent spirits met together, in response to this need, in April 1918, and a dozen others soon joined in the effort to determine, in the midst of war, the essentials of an enduring peace. As a first step, a seminar was arranged throughout the summer to define and discuss the issues which must be met in the conference finally assembled to bring peace to the world. It was decided to call these issues "war aims," to conform to the ruling preoccupation of the time, and to call the group, for the moment, the "Committee on Nothing at All." It had the nucleus of the old American Union Against Militarism.

After the Armistice, the "war aims" became "peace aims." The bans lifted, the discussion could once more be open. Before the end of November, the Committee on Nothing at All had become the League of Free Nations Association (soon the Foreign Policy Association), with a national membership representing many groups and professions, united in the belief that: —

The League of Nations must be democratic; it must have its parliament; it must be open to all free nations; it must be organized now; it must have administrative machinery; and it must include a bill of rights for nations, giving to all equal access to the sea, to raw materials, to new countries or colonies, to rivers, railways, and canals.

We were one of the few American organizations that sent to the Peace Conference an expression of its conviction at every stage of the deliberations, throwing our emphasis on a democratic, not a militaristic, peace.

Though so many informed and influential groups remained silent as the treaty-making went forward, this same impulse was evidently felt by simple people who sensed how much they had at stake in the outcome, though they had no academic approach to diplomacy — rather, they visualized the assemblage at Versailles in the terms of their own little gatherings. Thus I find in my files a copy of a cablegram sent by neighbors on Henry Street in those fateful weeks of 1919: —

SIDEWALKS

President Wilson
Paris

We, people in one block on the East Side, organized as a Community Council, congratulate you for making a League of Nations. We know you will stand by your declaration that all nations shall be members, just as we formed this league of neighbors. There can be no real peace of peoples unless Russia's Soviet has a share. We ask you to stand by Russia.

M —— T ——
Block Captain

I was in Paris while the peace negotiations were in process, and felt there some of the non-militaristic influences that were trying — how vainly the event proved — to make themselves felt. Kerenski spoke to me, without bitterness, of his experience and of his hope for Russia in a world at peace. Louis Marshall was there, trying to see that the interest of the Jews was not lost to sight. And there were many others, whose names are written in the history of that tragic period. The man who seemed to me the most arresting personality was Nansen, called by Romain Rolland "the only hero of the War." He could not give up his hope that children would be fed, no matter on which side the armies fought.

"Woodrow Wilson" was, of course, the name on everyone's lips; though then it was not spoken with the reverence and complete trust with which it was uttered when the President first arrived in Europe.

I risk repeating a comment that is known. During the negotiations a cartoon appeared in a German paper showing a heavenly cloud hovering over a tiny mortal figure. Out of the cloud issues a voice, saying, "They are n't paying much attention to your Fourteen Points, are they, Wilson?" And the mortal replies, "No, and they never did to your Ten."

Mr. Wilson was incomparable in his ability to formulate social and political ideals and aspirations for the student mind. Perhaps it was this very quality which gave him eminence, but which made it the more difficult for him to meet and to combat the danger points of intrigue and deception inevitably associated with war and diplomacy. Mornings and afternoons, and sometimes evenings, too, disappointed unofficial observers and members of the press called at the hotel and almost wept because of their dismay, their certainty, that Woodrow Wilson was no match at the diplomatic table for Clemenceau and Lloyd George.

Though there was a general disinclination to question the Peace Treaty after it was drafted, a membership vote supported the conviction of a minority in the executive committee of the Foreign Policy Association that the Treaty terms called for a free and full and public discussion. During the War, most of the peace organizations had become inactive. The League to Enforce Peace, which had continued, was interested in the machinery of international action. But the Foreign Policy Association did not hesitate to draw attention to the gap between the Fourteen Points and the Versailles Treaty. Even so, some serious flaws in the first draft had been rectified, weak points strengthened, harsh and stupid points liberalized; and we felt that our espousal of changes had been one factor in bringing about these results.

Progress toward international peace or toward any social goal runs in a current in which three streams are mingled. There must be the flow of emotion, — what has been called the "moral urge," — springing from desire for the good to be gained, abhorrence of the evil that bars the way; there must be clear and comprehensive understanding of the factors in the situation, and their relationships; there must be a plan of affirmative action, and the marshaling of forces to carry it through.

I seem justified in dwelling in detail on these incidents, for the motivation of our efforts was an overpowering sense of peril to all held dear by true Americans, which drove our group to act to the limit of strength and ability in the negotiations for peace, even in the midst of war. We found that an organization of people deeply sincere, guided by a vision of what the world might be, and with assurance enough to act, can influence opinion and events.

It seems to me that the experience of those years has a bearing on to-day's happenings. What are we talking about now? We want conference instead of war. Then, we were sending armies instead of conferring. The disparaged "pre-War liberals" who banded themselves together as the American Union Against Militarism suggested a technique to be adapted to a given international situation. It was applied in the Mexican crisis; and it helped resolve that difficulty. It applies to-day. It is a method long affirmed by social organizations like the settlements, and more and more recognized by statesmen and diplomats. The day is bound to come when it will not be possible to ignore it as preliminary to any attempts to formalize agreed relations between governments. In conversations between nations, the simple directness that has been found most useful between neighbors is more and more the method approved.

XIII

A LOOK BACK AND A LOOK AHEAD

WHAT has been written in the chapters of this book will have lost significance if a consciousness of sin in our human relations and a quite general impulse to do better have not been recorded.

The primary offense of those who are the most vocal champions of the achievement of our civilization has doubtless been the complacent optimism that progress has been impressive enough to justify the claim that "all's well in the world," particularly in rich America. This sentiment has not been shared by the social workers, whose object, singly or in organized groups, to help relieve want and suffering has not protected them in recent years from the realization that their efforts cannot achieve their goal without basic and constructive social change.   To read the conference proceedings and the writings of those engaged in measures to ameliorate and to educate is to find that the people who are actively working in the several fields are vigorous in their rejection of easy panaceas; nor do they express any complete satisfaction with their own contributions. This is not unusual or new.   I am sure that those who protected the runaway slaves, and at the same time labored strenuously for the abolition of slavery, were convinced that the rescue of the individual victim was of slight consequence compared with the advancement of cause and principle.

The change of the times, the tremendously augmented knowledge of conditions, the humiliation of finding the relative unimportance of worshiped gods, and the revelation brought by receding fortunes and unemployment, are developing an unprecedented technique of revolution, and revolution itself, which ten years ago would have seemed incredible.   It is being accomplished, not through hatred and blood sacrifice, but through a conviction of the actual relationships of individuals and nations, each to the other, economically, culturally, and politically; through the understanding that isolation is not possible to any race or people, even to any individual.

This account of what we have seen through the windows on Henry Street is far from an historical review; but our forty years have witnessed the inception of measures that helped prepare for the New Deal.   Many phases of to-day's developments go back to causes furthered by ardent crusaders whose hope and effort long appeared futile.   One step ahead and two steps back were often the course of progress, — or so it seemed, — but now each forward impulse appears as a link in what we measure as advancement.

Three books [1] were selected by the president of the National Conference of Social Work, on its fiftieth anniversary (1923), as three milestones of social progress. Each publication, it was judged, marked distinctly the attitude of its period to social perplexities, or perhaps to the changing circumstances.   Even the nomenclature current in the periods represented — 1872, 1890, 1915 — was indicative of the prevailing convictions of the time among social thinkers.   Retrospect is encouraging, and I have little doubt that measures of equalization of opportunities, contraction of distances between the children of one part of the city and another, language that is more widely understood and that reverberates in many circles, give more important meaning to Israel Zangwill's phrase, "the melting pot."

Protective measures that once seemed merely eleemosynary, beyond the obligations of law and outside the ken of Board of Estimate budgets, are now the planks of even the reactionary political platforms.

The times have produced men and women who measure the success of their endeavor not by enunciation but by success in translating aspirations into workable easement of the situation.   The future of relief methods is a question of vital importance.   Needless to repeat what

[1] *Dangerous Classes of New York and Twenty Years' Work among Them*, by Charles Loring Brace (Wynkoop, 1872); *How the Other Half Lives*, by Jacob Riis (Macmillan, 1890); *The House on Henry Street*, by Lillian D. Wald (Holt, 1915).

has been written in preceding pages of this book. All the steps that have been taken hitherto by expert social workers and philanthropists of statesmanlike qualities lead inevitably to the recognition of a minimum standard of living throughout the country, below which no one shall be allowed to drop. Our republic cannot reach its fulfillment without recognizing that economically it cannot exist "half slave and half free." The depression may have been that never-welcomed visitation, a blessing in disguise, for certainly both the courage and the constructive efficiency of the Administration in trying to meet the disastrous epidemic of unemployment and all its complications are a priceless gain. To find men and women trained and expert for the administration of national relief plans under the steadying hand of Harry Hopkins is a source of congratulation.

Children have lost nothing of their charm and their appeal by their emergence as most urgent factors in securing a more reasoned and equitable society.

And young people show their awareness of a changing world which has affected disastrously more lives than were scarred by the World War. They face conditions that dissipate their dream of importance and usefulness on their graduation, and their careful training seems to go for naught. I think the things social workers have been talking of so long seem very real to youth to-day, though they seemed impossible before.

During the "jazz" period we did not realize what is now clearer — that our much-criticized young people often gave better account of themselves than did their elders. In those hysterical years, the emphasis on sex was rankly expressed, and cherished shrines often were ruthlessly and contemptuously destroyed; but only an inflexible watcher of the times could have failed to see the advantage of frankness over the hypocrisy and surreptitious experiment that so generally characterized sex behavior in the pre-War years. "Self-expression" seemed for a time to justify lawlessness and was a damaging slogan, few people having the courage to acknowledge that it was an excuse to break down "control" and very little else.   Faced with the not surprising, usually inevitable consequences of their conduct, disciples of the new cult have been willing, even eager, to discuss their course and their philosophy with older friends who commanded respect.   I have heard from them no expression of any deep-rooted faith that the disparagement of the home or of family ties, implied in the practices they defended, would bring about better people, happier life, or a higher civilization.

The young people who gather at the Settlement, as well as those who occasionally visit it, are encouraging. If it were possible to chart their values against those of their elders, I believe that hope would be kindled in the hearts of true lovers of mankind.

In an earlier chapter I have dwelt upon the advances and needs of our educational system.   If there were no other indication of changing concepts of values, the advice given to students entering college in the fall of 1933 would proclaim a new and in some instances startling shift in point of view.

One president, at the first "assembly" of the year, said: "We are entering on an era when system and organization will be of greater and greater importance; it is the business of learning to explain and direct these systems."

And the head of one of our oldest and most respected universities admonished youth thus: "Never before in time of peace has the nation been so vividly aware of its own solidarity of interests. Never before was there a keener appreciation that industry and commerce and politics and religion and education must all be tested by their effects on man and the social order. No principle, or system, or institution, will be left untouched which cannot justify itself by the service it renders to society, and if it costs more than it is worth, judged by such standards, it will go."

I am not unaware that I am writing during the apparent supremacy of Hitler in Germany and at a time when, for the fifth winter, bread lines are forming in the richest city in the richest country in the world; but I am also aware that measures, until recently the hope of minorities, are now woven into the warp and woof of national legislation. Hitherto such drastic adjustments have been attempted only in time of war; but under a leader trained in social thinking and in the application of social principles, with associates of acknowledged capacity, and with no axes to grind, the country — for the time being, at any rate — has the courage and faith for new pioneering.

Internationally the outlook is more disturbing. Despite the united front against war among the plain people of the earth, as expressed through conferences not only of pacifists, but of college faculty and students, of labor bodies, of women's associations, of radical and temperate organizations, the cloud of war darkens the horizon and the German influence cannot be ignored. Many people regard the Chancellor as insane or neurotic, perhaps in part because through all his denunciations and illogical conclusions he has shown no gleam of humor; nevertheless his leadership seems for the moment to sway the German nation.

At no place in our own public life is youth's participation more encouraging than in stimulating thought and action in the direction of international peace. Before the Presidential election in 1932, representatives of the Women's International League for Peace and Freedom sought interviews with each candidate to learn if possible what international planks might be expected in the party platforms. What Mrs. Hannah Clothier Hull and I said when we called on President Hoover in the White House is unimportant. What the young college girl who accompanied us said was epochal: —

"Mr. President, many thousands of girls and boys like myself have just graduated from college. We face a world that has no use for us. In November we shall march to the polls for the first time in our lives to help elect a President. We are not much interested in prohibition, which seems to occupy the minds of the many. Drink is, after all, largely a personal question and seems to us of little relative importance. What does fill our minds and our hearts is the price that we, my generation, are paying for the mistakes and futility of the older generation. We want to vote for a candidate who will speak frankly and sincerely on issues involving

A Henry Street Leader

the possibility of future wars that we may be called upon to fight, and who will give us some assurance of economic stability on which we are dependent. We are not a young generation of emotional radicals, but we are an insistent generation, demanding of the old parties the courage and intelligence to meet the conditions of to-day with the methods of to-day."

The undertakings of the past months, the evident attempt to delve beneath the surface, the hope of eliminating causes as well as symptoms of distress, have aroused the genuine interest and coöperation of the American people. Perhaps this "bloodless revolution" is "the moral equivalent for war" that William James coveted for the world. What unprecedented values are disclosed, what vistas open up, as the horizon widens, the interests multiply! No war ever enabled us to see, as does the present effort, the human relationships, or so filled a people with the impulse to save, not to destroy.

The newer concept of the obligation of the State to the economic security of the industrial worker bids fair to uproot the old American persuasion that success is a matter of individual effort. Until this depression, the first reaction of men in the world of affairs has been that there is something wrong with anyone who fails to "make good."

I recall my embarrassment one day when showing the House to visitors, among them two college professors. In the presence of a group of girls obviously not from homes of luxury, one remarked, "I am so much in sympathy with this settlement because of its care of the sick. Of course people cannot help illness [sic], but

I am sure that in this land of wealth and opportunity no one need be poor and jobless." It was a far cry from that shortsighted comment to the words of another college professor,[2] spokesman for the present Administration: —

"There is a test by which all our present efforts must in the end be judged: unless we can make people feel again that for the man who wants to work will be provided work; unless the ordinary man is assured that by a balanced allocation of enterprise he will possess a decent standard of living if he does his part, we shall have failed." And he added, "We must not assure him of this with words, but with jobs."

In comparing the past and the present, an impressive illustration is to be found in the once "sweated" clothing industry, out of which has emerged the dynamic leadership of Sidney Hillman. There intelligent, honest union control has raised the living standard of the members not only in theory but in fact. Unfortunately, it must not be forgotten that other industries have a less heartening record. Years ago, long before the historic "Pittsburgh Survey," even the laity (meaning those not concerned about labor standards) were unhappy over what some had seen, what more had heard, of steel workers. Public attention has been focused upon conditions in that industry, and though some of the worst abuses have been rectified, the hearings in Washington on the steel code in July disclosed disturbing if not shocking disregard of human necessities.

The efforts of the government to-day have the co-

[2] Rexford Guy Tugwell.

operation of employers as well as of wage earners. Distinguished industrial leaders participate in the united effort to bring the New Deal to fulfillment. Gerard Swope, of General Electric, has been one of the foremost spokesmen for economic planning and for unemployment insurance. His part is important, as is Sidney Hillman's, in the march toward the coveted goal — better opportunity, increased security for employer, employee, and consumer. For the wage earner's economic stability is interlocked with stability of employment, and both with the integrity of the government. Each is part of a whole; but the government alone has power to eliminate cutthroat competition, which has never brought lasting good fortune to producer or consumer. To keep this before the public is a great educational service, the more effective if, instead of being expressed in terms of emergency projects, it is integrated with democratic philosophy and method. Nor is it too much to say that, while there is a moral compulsion to fall into line to-day, it is not an emotional compulsion. It is based upon expert testimony, upon study of all the factors involved in our complex situation. The appeal is not to passion, but to reason.

The world is watching this unprecedented adventure. It is in reality a serious attempt to explore the possibilities of our political philosophy. Perhaps the alleged failure of democracy can be explained by the fact that democracy has not been tried. Are not the doubters akin to shipwrecked Sambo? The ship had perished with all aboard her except the captain and Sambo, who were adrift in a lifeboat. Said the captain: —

"Sambo, I must sleep a bit.   See that star?" pointing to the north.   "Steer the boat with your eye on that, and all will be well."   But a storm arose, and Sambo, frightened, shook the captain, crying: —

"Cap'n, Cap'n, wake up!   Give me another star! I'se lost dis one."

In a recent visit to me after having been in Washington, Margaret Bondfield, a watchful, seasoned student of world movements, at one time a distinguished member of the British Cabinet, commented on the phenomenon of our methods to-day: —

"By a stroke of the President's pen [in signing the cotton textile code] America caught up with and passed the point reached in England as a result of more than eighty years of strenuous effort.   The world will watch to see how much of this improvised structure will become permanent.   And," added this keen observer, "it is too much to hope that such a gigantic revolution can be carried through without some disasters and mistakes; but enough should remain to make this period stand out as a turning point and a great advance in the history of the United States.   Its influence will be felt throughout the world."

As time marks progress, only the neophyte would expect quicker motion than has characterized the recent past.   At a celebration toward the end of 1924, an outstanding leader in American life wished for Florence Kelley, the guest of the occasion, that she "might live to see no children in America left unprotected by Congressional legislation, no women engaged in night work, no more girls working without the protection of the minimum wage, no old men contemplating suicide because we have no provision against unemployment and indigent old age." In the few years since 1924, even the cynic cannot fail to see progress toward this not unreasonable goal, though dear Florence Kelley is not here to rejoice with us in the gains now written into legislation.

How quickly we *are* moving can perhaps be glimpsed only by people situated as are we, where one is made aware of the centuries that separate, but also of the bridges of friendship which are built — and enduring bridges, too. No bridge, however, is comparable to that erected by the sympathetic nurses, who gather in their work tales of romance and superstition from the background of many of the homes they enter.

While applying the latest technique in maternity care, one such nurse, inquiring of the patriarchal grandfather the origins of the "Lilith" legend, was thus enlightened: —

"It is not for women to know, but you have been so good I shall say this: Eva was the wife of man for the cooking and bearing of children, but Lilith was the wife of his spirit."

And a block or two away a Chinaman told of the "dleam wife made by the Gleat Dlagon fo' the Emplo [Emperor]. That wife always young, always plitty, always have boys."

Soon the color and delight of living even momentarily with the ancients will vanish. Their traditions may seem a barrier to understanding, and yet from such soil

folk tale and poetry have grown, enriching life.   Often
the modern mind derives a balance and perspective from
this lore and a heightened power of creative expression
as escape from the day's round.

It is curious to realize that this summary of less than
two decades reaches into the period when women had no
voice in government.   Women themselves have played
an important part in broadening their traditional responsibilities — the welfare of children and the home —
to the important place these obligations now hold in
"the new society."   This greater rôle of the home
maker has demonstrated brilliantly woman's ability as
organizer.

A friend who conscientiously studies and supports
local, national, and international efforts on behalf of the
underprivileged often voices the conviction that the
mythical farsighted "Man from Mars" would not hesitate to single out the women of this age, and particularly of this country, for the importance of their
achievements.

The United States Children's Bureau is the apotheosis
of a flexible public agency under statesmanlike administration, never diverted from a single objective: to secure
for the children recognition as national treasure concerning which everything should be known, publicized,
and ministered unto, so far as is humanly possible.   The
Bureau, moreover, demonstrates the vigilance and the
marked ability of two outstanding women, Julia La-
throp, who organized it, and her successor, Grace Ab-

bott. They, like other successful mothers, have performed miracles of thrift, declaring large dividends on minute budgets.

Frances Perkins brings to the Cabinet as Secretary of Labor the many years of training and experience which step by step have rounded out the preparation for her great responsibility. Even with the contribution of her vivid personality, the press, generally speaking, pays her the tribute of reporting the wisdom of the words and acts rather than idle "gossip" about the "first woman Cabinet member."

Those who know the Colorado coal industry know the courage of Josephine Roche, whose social training prepared her to accept the controlling interest in an important mining property that came to her by inheritance. In a year when her chief competitor has gone into receivership, her company shows a profit in spite — many will join her in believing because — of the fact of the coöperation between management and union in the conduct of the business.

Of Florence Kelley's great contribution I have already spoken. Those who knew her know what her pride would be in the active workers she helped train — Frances Perkins, Josephine and Pauline Goldmark, Mary Dewson, and the others of that effective group. It was Josephine Goldmark who prepared the brief for the famous "Oregon Case," where a lawyer (her brother-in-law, Louis D. Brandeis) argued the case, not on legal technicalities and precedent, but on reasons of health and humanity. The decision settled for all time the right of our legislatures to limit the working hours of women — the first rumble of the revolution which was to rate human welfare above machine-made profits.

In a settlement one deals with the extremes. Women active in civic groups and in public life turn to us for coöperation, sometimes for counsel. But we are called on, too, by neighbors facing primitive problems, like the really troubled housewife who came to me because she had "secret wealth" amounting, as I recall it, to two thousand dollars. Her husband never gave her money for the household expenses, but required exact specifications. The frightened woman explained: —

"I used to keep awake nights, for I had not a dollar of my own and he never told me if he had any, and I was scared to be without anything and maybe if he died I 'd have to go for charity. So, many years ago, when I asked for money for a pound of coffee or some tea or for sugar or anything, I 'd take out a cup or a pinch and hide it; and then when there was enough to make up what I asked for, I 'd take the stuff from its hiding place and put the money away. I never spent a penny for myself. I just put it safe away for when I might be alone and without money. And," concluded the harassed woman, "now maybe I 'll die first, and what shall I do about all that money?" Nor was this our only encounter with this kind of enslavement of womanhood by "the master of the house."

Perhaps no change in American life in recent years is more dramatic than that affecting the Negroes. Eminent Negro leaders are well known, but few realize how large is the intelligentsia — the writers, editors, poets, dramatists, painters, musicians, doctors, nurses, social workers — who would rank high in any society. Evidences of their progress are the dignity and self-respect which come to people who know that there is a place for them earned by their merits, despite ancient prejudice and social ostracism.   There is much to be done, — much searching of the heart, — but there has also been an almost unbelievable change in attitude between the time when first we knew them and their situation to-day.   It is no longer the isolated white man or woman who shares with them the sense of common interests and purposes, but a large and growing group. Modern Negro literature, research, and writing of colored students of social affairs are promises of more universal understanding of the situation.   Some sections of the country are indifferent to the progress of the race, or ignorant of it.   They need to be infiltrated with views that would ensure a safer relationship between the two races.   The irritating debate on "social equality" has little or nothing to do with social justice.

One of the gifted supervisors on the Henry Street staff is a colored nurse who stands high in the regard of her colleagues of both races; and after all, it is not so very long since Henry Street was the first organization to employ on its staff on equal terms the Negro woman who desired thus to serve the sick.

The immigration restrictions have many more facets of interest than the turning away of undesirables or the "Red Scares" stirred up by oversolicitous "patriots." And humor, as always, accompanies the pathos.   A telephone call to my country home informed me that the "Organized Wives of America" wished my help in getting their husbands over. They were really in distress because, though they were citizens in their own rights, their alien husbands did not come within the quota and were languishing on other shores. The Cable Act made the position of the foreign wife more difficult, since she no longer automatically acquires the citizenship of her American husband, though it simplifies things for the American wife who marries a citizen of another country.

There is an important change in the fact that many immigrants, particularly the Italians, now return to their old homes for good. There have been years when the number leaving the United States was greater than the number coming in. This is due in part, of course, to widespread unemployment here, as well as to the difficulty of returning to the United States under the present regulations.

After all, the spirit of the times calls for deep thought and for new measuring rods. It challenges the privileged to ponder on why and how — and to what purpose. It calls to defense the old economists and defenders of political faiths. And this spirit, which is both young and old, expresses the conviction of the rights of every human being. It calls for the active, intelligent participation of every man and woman — not merely their acquiescence — in a new society.

The consequences of war of course accelerated today's crisis, but to the initiate the change in the relationships of people and of nations, in the consciousness of the importance to society of the individual (even the least cultured), has been a long, slow process. The change has been brought about by faith in "the masses," and in their potential power for good if accorded a place in the sun, not as a beneficent gift from the powerful to the lowly, but as inherent in the political philosophy and religious belief of the thinking and the good.

No person living who exercises his opportunities to read, to listen, to feel, or to see can fail to be cognizant of the reality of these changes. Strange as it may seem to future students of this era, I think there cannot be many people to-day who do not apprehend its difficulties, who can fail to understand that education is slow and that, despite the selfless devotion of many great Americans, we are not vouchsafed a miracle, but something better — the opportunity to work out for ourselves a planned and controlled way of life.

In these social changes, slow and swift, settlements play their part. Never in all the years have we on Henry Street doubted the validity of our belief in the essential dignity of man and the obligations of each generation to do better for the oncoming generation.

A social economist recently said, "Settlements correspond more to many needs than any other form of social organization. If there were no settlements in our cities to-day, we should have to start them; there never was greater need of them than now, for effectively bridging the gaps between social groups and economic levels."

It seems worth observing that people who are interested in understanding and helping direct these social forces are not necessarily dull and dreary. In all the world I have found no group with more sparkle, more

ability to abandon themselves to genuine good times,
than the people who are not absorbed in their small
cosmos. How infantile are the things with which
bored, blasé people try to amuse themselves! Let's
wipe out the picture of the "dull" life of "the people
who care." I have known very few who were not en-
dowed with imaginative sensibility and humor; none
who carried over a message without these attributes.
The flashing wit of a colleague has seemed often to be
the beam that shed light on dark places when argument
and reason failed.

It has been my good fortune to know the fellowship
of men and women from many lands, many circles, and
with inherited variations of traditions and religious influences. Presidents and prime ministers, the leaders
or the martyrs of their day from Ireland, Britain, Russia,
Poland, Czechoslovakia, Italy, Mexico, India, have found
their way to the House, not because of any material
quest, but to seek sympathetic understanding of their
desires for a freer life for their fellow men. And we
on Henry Street have become internationalists, not
through the written word or through abstract theses,
but because we have found that the problems of one set
of people are essentially the problems of all. We have
found that the things which make men alike are finer
and stronger than the things which make them different, and that the vision which long since proclaimed
the interdependence and the kinship of mankind was
farsighted and is true.

All the varied experience of intercourse with the many
races, those who are expressive and those who are not,

and who wait upon others for a formulation of what lies deep within their racial traditions or religious promises — such experience points to the inevitable: that people rise and fall together, that no one group or nation dare be an economic or a social law unto itself. That has been the lesson we have learned in the years on Henry Street.

INDEX

INDEX